try it!

MEDITERRANEAN PALEO DIET

try it!

MEDITERRANEAN PALEO DIET

Contents

Introduction

It's easy to find convincing studies or research to support eating one way or another. Around every corner is another outrageous claim that one particular way of eating is the healthiest, with a list of "dos and don'ts" that must be adhered to religiously. While some fad diets roar into the spotlight with sweeping evidence of superiority, some simply stand the test of time, because many of the tenets produce healthy results for a lot of people.

Both the Mediterranean and Paleo diets have been touted as ways to healthier eating. While the Mediterranean diet holds the favour of many within the medical community for its proven heart-health and brain-boosting properties, the Paleo diet has also shown to provide tremendous benefit for reducing systemic inflammation and corresponding conditions. With both sides fighting for dominance in the nutrition world, could there be a way to combine these diets into a lifestyle of eating that's both sustainable in the long term and capable of producing both sets of health benefits? There is.

This book fuses these two diets into one cohesive approach, with a collection of fresh and simple recipes. By focusing on seasonal fruits and vegetables; natural vegetable fats; and plenty of nuts, seeds, and lean protein, the Mediterranean Paleo diet blends both worlds together for a new and delicious way to eat.

The Mediterranean
Paleo Diet

The word *diet* often conjures images of limited food lists, hunger pangs, and constant cravings for more satisfying foods. The Mediterranean Paleo diet, on the other hand, promotes a huge variety of the freshest fruits and vegetables; hunger-quenching fats; and a vast array of quality meat and responsibly-sourced seafood. In this chapter, you find out just what the Mediterranean Paleo diet is, what it can do for your health, and how you can reap the benefits.

What Is the **Mediterranean Paleo Diet?**

The Mediterranean Paleo diet is a **diverse** and **nourishing** way to eat that promotes long-standing **heart, brain,** and **anti-inflammatory** benefits. It supplies a variety of **fruits** and **vegetables; lean proteins** and **fish;** and **plant-based fats, nuts, and seeds.** This long-term lifestyle combines two popular approaches into one plan that can be tailored to your personal needs and goals.

The Mediterranean Diet

Years of research and numerous medical studies have supported the Mediterranean-style diet as an optimally healthy way to eat. However, this approach relies heavily on grains (such as wheat and rice) and legumes (such as beans, lentils, and soy). Most grains are refined in a modern diet and no longer provide the same nutritional benefits as whole-grain versions. Consuming grains and legumes has been linked to an increased inflammatory response that can lead to further digestive and autoimmune problems.

While these food do provide an important source of complex carbohydrates, similar nutrients can also be consumed through starchy tubers and other root vegetables, nuts, and seeds.

WHOLE GRAINS

NUTS/SEEDS

FISH/SEAFOOD

BEANS/LEGUMES

POULTRY

LIMITED DAIRY

FRUIT

Eating the Mediterranean Paleo Way

The Mediterranean Paleo diet seamlessly merges the overlapping food of both plans into one inarguably beneficial approach to eating. The excessive red meat and saturated animal fats of the Paleo diet that can cause long-term heart problems are eliminated, along with the grains and legumes that can cause inflammation on the Mediterranean diet. The primary components then shift to focus on the food proven to promote long-term benefits – fruits, vegetables, fish, lean proteins, and healthy fats.

High-quality foods are key to this diet approach, so you're encouraged to eat fresh, local, seasonal, chemical-free food whenever possible. This means looking for quality pasture-raised meat and eggs without additives, antibiotics, or preservatives, and avoiding pre-packaged food that often contain added sugars, stabilizers, or modifiers. This book provides a general guide that can be modified for individual calorie, nutrient, and weight-loss needs, according to what your personal medical professional recommends.

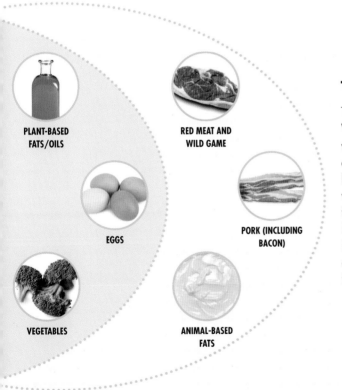

PLANT-BASED FATS/OILS

RED MEAT AND WILD GAME

EGGS

PORK (INCLUDING BACON)

VEGETABLES

ANIMAL-BASED FATS

The Paleo Diet

The Paleo diet relies heavily on animal-based food. While leaner cuts of meat are emphasized, many who follow this diet consume the majority of their daily calories from meat – including wild game, grass-fed beef, pork, and bacon, chicken, and seafood, along with ample amounts of lard and tallow. When you factor in the high price of quality meat, this approach becomes expensive for the consumer. The fact that the Paleo diet also limits or eliminates carbohydrates of all forms (such as whole grains and legumes) makes following the plan difficult in the long term.

Why Should I **Eat This Way?**

Everyone is motivated differently when it comes to dieting. Whether it's for long-term health benefits, weight loss, or relief from inflammatory conditions and allergies, following the components of the Mediterranean Paleo diet can help you meet your personal goals.

A HEALTHIER BODY

Along with moderate daily physical exercise, diets high in fruits and vegetables, nuts and seeds, fish, and olive oil, with minimal dairy and red meat – such as the Mediterranean Paleo diet – have been proven to help prevent type 2 diabetes, heart disease, and strokes. Followers of this eating style have also benefited from a reduced risk of Alzheimer's disease, dementia, and Parkinson's disease.

REDUCED INFLAMMATION

Inflammation can wreak havoc on major body systems. While it's a primary immune response that's critical to healing, prolonged inflammation may play a part in joint pain, chronic fatigue, obesity, and even cancer. This diet is overflowing with omega-3 fatty acids, fibre-rich vegetables, and dark leafy greens – foods that have been shown to reduce systemic inflammation.

INCREASED ENERGY

Eliminating processed food can lead to increased energy, as your body no longer has to process and detoxify from these products. Many Paleo diet followers report an increase in focus and concentration – along with a tremendous increase in energy – when consuming cleaner, unrefined, and unprocessed food. Fresh, ripe, in-season fruits and vegetables are also the most nutrient-dense, supplying an immediate source of energy for your body to use.

A LEANER BODY

While diet fizzy drinks, non-fat dressings, and low-fat potato crisps may seem like waist-reducing choices, they're loaded with refined sugars that can actually have the opposite effect. Refined grains, sugars, and processed oils have been shown to be major factors in weight gain. By eliminating these common offenders, the Mediterranean Paleo diet offers an alternative that is high in fibre and natural plant-based fats that can help you shed those extra pounds.

Calorie Intake and Movement

Making the transition to a healthier lifestyle like the Mediterranean Paleo diet requires a shift in thinking. You'll change how you shop for food, figure out what recipes you like, and learn what you want to incorporate into your meals.

And if you're looking to lose weight, you'll also have to make changes not only to *what* you eat, but also to *how* you eat. Because weight loss has a lot to do with calorie consumption, you have to create a calorie deficit to lose weight, taking in fewer calories than you burn. It's easy to do this with portion control – for example, using smaller plates and then eating only what you put on your plate. You can also use the calorie counts for the recipes in this book to track how much you eat throughout the day.

Along with the food component, the Mediterranean Paleo diet – like every diet plan – should be accompanied by a moderate amount of daily movement. Many studies have shown that gentle exercise at any age can improve overall health and wellbeing by increasing blood and oxygen flow, strengthening bones, and alleviating stress. While it takes effort to work physical activity into your day, doing so helps your physical and mental health.

Choosing the **Right Food**

As with any diet change, you set yourself up for **success** by having an understanding of the **appropriate food** for it, as well as the ones you should **limit** or **avoid.** The following categories can get you started on the right path.

Food to Eat

The Mediterranean Paleo diet includes a rich variety of food to get a broad range of nutrients. The images show some great choices to provide the bulk of your dietary intake. Make sure to eat plenty of servings of fruits, vegetables, nuts, seeds, eggs, and olive oil daily. Fish and lean poultry should be consumed at least twice a week.

FRESH, SEASONAL VEGETABLES OF ALL KINDS

NUTS AND SEEDS

EGGS

FISH AND SEAFOOD

RIPE FRUITS

LEAN, UNCURED POULTRY

PURE, HIGH-QUALITY OLIVE OIL

FRESH HERBS

DRIED SPICES

A Note on Red Wine

While a 140g (5-ounce) glass of red wine daily is often an acceptable part of the Mediterranean diet, alcohol of any kind is typically considered a toxin on the Paleo diet. The health effects of alcohol are highly debated within the medical community, but a small amount of alcohol has been shown to reduce the risk of heart disease in some studies. Because of these cardiovascular benefits, it remains on the list of acceptable but limited food for the Mediterranean Paleo diet.

Food to Limit

While these food are allowed on the Mediterranean Paleo diet, they are best consumed in smaller quantities, or on occasion.

Full-fat dairy

Cured meat

Red meat (limit to three to four times per month)

Salt

Honey and natural sweeteners

Animal fats, such as lard, tallow, and ghee

Caffeine

Alcohol

Food to Avoid

These food are best avoided while following the Paleo Mediterranean diet. Make sure to look carefully at the packaging for any such hidden ingredients.

Refined sugars

Refined grains

Partially hydrogenated oils

Margarine

Additives, modifiers, and chemical preservatives

Poor-quality or highly-processed meat and seafood

Legumes, such as beans, lentils, and peanuts

Sourcing Your Ingredients
Responsibly

As fewer people become responsible for providing food for more people, it's important to understand how purchasing choices affect the greater agricultural and environmental communities. Here's a quick guide to making smart food choices that help consumers, suppliers, and the environment.

Fruits and Vegetables

Because fruits and vegetables make up so much of the Mediterranean Paleo diet, it's especially important to ask several questions before buying these goods: has this produce come into contact with chemicals that could transfer to you? How far did it have to travel to get to your table? Is it from a farm that's mindful of sustainable farming practices and fair wages? Is there something else you can use that's local or in season?

While it's difficult and unrealistic to follow all of these practices for every fruit and vegetable purchase, it's possible to keep them in mind while shopping, and to make every responsible choice given the circumstances. Determine what the most important factors are to you, do some local research, and shop accordingly.

Meat

Meat production has a tremendous environmental impact globally. Large-scale meat production is one of the biggest contributors to greenhouse gas emissions; it uses heavy amounts of fossil fuels, water, land, and antibiotics. But meat is also an important part of the food chain and offers many vital nutrients to its consumers. Bearing all of this in mind, it's important to eat meat responsibly. Always look for meat that's antibiotic-free, pastured or grass-fed, and humanely raised. Avoid meat that has been injected with brines or sugar water, has added nitrites, or has been highly processed. And as a respectful practice, try to find ways you can incorporate lesser-known cuts or organ meat into your diet to encourage consumption of the entire animal.

Fats and Oils

Extra-virgin olive oil is a staple ingredient for Mediterranean Paleo eaters, so stocking up on a good supply of decent-quality oil will go a long way in the success of these recipes. Many of the cheapest brands are not 100 per cent, pure, pressed olive oil, so make sure to do a little research before heading to the supermarket to see which brands are suitable and available. You may wish to have a more economical olive oil for general cooking and a more flavourful oil to drizzle over salads and fresh vegetables.

Some recipes in this book call for coconut oil. As a saturated fat, it can be a controversial ingredient. However, its ability to act as a dairy substitute is beneficial, so it has been included.

Seafood

As the world population increases, so does the demand for sustainable supplies of seafood. Years of irresponsible fishing and other harvesting practices have destroyed many of the once-thriving ocean and river habitats necessary to support fish populations. The good news is that every region still has seafood resources that are abundant or appropriately farmed. Ask your fishmonger how they promote sustainable fishing practices, and purchase accordingly. Look for sustainable sources of sea bass, halibut, prawn, or tuna, and avoid red snapper, orange roughy, and swordfish.

Nuts and Seeds

Nuts and seeds are great resources for healthy omega-3 fats and are a quick and filling way to add extra calories to a plant-based meal. Always look for unsalted nuts to limit sodium intake. To get the most flavour, nuts can be lightly toasted. Simply place nuts in a small pan over medium-low heat, stirring constantly, for 3 to 5 minutes, or until fragrant. Once toasted, remove nuts from the hot pan to cool completely before storing them in an airtight container.

Seasonal and Local

To be the most responsible consumer, learn what's seasonally available and local. These products are often the highest in nutritional value because they are fresh and don't waste time, money, and non-renewable resources in long transport. They are also often the most economical choices because they are widely available during the "on" season. An easy way to learn what's currently in season is to shop at a local farmer's market and take note of what fruits and vegetables are available to purchase at certain times throughout the growing year. However, bear in mind this will vary from region to region.

planning
ahead

There's no better way to succeed with a new diet than to plan ahead! This chapter goes over common variations and substitutions, frequently used spices and mixtures, and essential cooking equipment. It also includes two seasonal meal plans with shopping lists to guide you.

Variations and **Substitutions**

For success on long-term diets like the Mediterranean Paleo diet, nutritionists recommend an 80/20 rule, with strict adherence 80 per cent of the time, and the remaining 20 per cent allowing variations or substitutions. These are some common variations to cover that 20 per cent that may help you stay on track.

Dairy

Dairy is a controversial food for some. If you're lactose-intolerant, it should be avoided. If not, you may wish to consume small amounts of full-fat, quality dairy products, such at yogurt, kefir, butter, and cheese. Always look for products from antibiotic-free, pastured, and grass-fed cows, sheep, or goats. The probiotics found in cultured yogurt, kefir, and some fresh curd cheeses are extremely beneficial for the bacteria in your intestinal tract.

In most recipes, coconut oil can be substituted for butter, and coconut milk can be substituted for cream, as indicated in ingredients lists. A recipe for coconut milk yogurt is also included for those who wish to eliminate dairy completely.

Red Meat

While red meat is still encouraged on the Mediterranean Paleo diet, it's restricted to three to four servings per month to stay in step with the amounts used in Mediterranean diet heart-health studies. If you find your blood pressure and cholesterol remain at healthy levels, you may wish to increase your red meat consumption. If not, you can get plenty of iron daily from dark, leafy greens.

Bread and Pasta

Many types of bread and pasta are made with refined and highly processed grains. They also contain gluten, a controversial protein that can be extremely hazardous for those who suffer from coeliac disease and other inflammatory digestive ailments.

As an alternative way to eliminate these processed grains and gluten, this book provides a chapter of recipes using vegetable-based pasta. It also includes several recipes for bread, crêpes, and cakes that offer an alternative for those who wish to eliminate these products 100 per cent of the time.

For those who have no adverse reaction to standard bread, you may find that simply moderating portion sizes allows you to keep sprouted and whole-grain versions in your diet on occasion.

VEGETABLE PASTA
A great alternative to traditional processed-grain pastas.

Whole Grains and Legumes

Some may question why whole grains and legumes aren't a huge part of the Mediterranean Paleo diet. While the Mediterranean diet embraces them wholeheartedly, the Paleo diet decidedly does not.

Whole grains and legumes can be an extremely economical source for protein, carbohydrates, fibre, and other essential nutrients. But some skeptics question the ability of our guts to fully absorb and digest these nutrients without sprouting or fermenting first, leading to a fairly strong inflammatory response. Legumes are also a high-carbohydrate source of protein.

For these reasons, whole grains and legumes aren't included in any of the recipes in this book. If you find they fit with your economical or nutritional needs, feel free to include them in moderation as part of your diet.

Special Diets

As with all diets, you have certain allowances for special conditions. Some people require low-glycaemic, high-fibre, or gluten-free diets. Athletes and nursing mothers need more calories than kids or those with a more sedentary lifestyle, and some people have particular allergies to certain food. To cater to different needs, all of the recipes in this book are cane-sugar free, and wheat- and gluten-free; many are also low carb, dairy-free, vegan, or vegetarian. Seek the advice of a medical professional for your individual diet needs.

What About Pork?

For this book, pork is used sparingly. Bacon, ham, and sausage are high in saturated fat and often contain sugar as part of the curing or processing. This meat does add a distinct flavour, however, so enjoy it in moderation.

Herbs and **Spices**

Fresh herbs and spices make a world of difference in simple recipes. From the distinct flavour of fresh basil to the complex aroma of ras el hanout, these additions can make any dish shine. While herbs are delicious fresh or dried, try to use fresh herbs whenever possible to get the most antioxidants and inflammation-reducing effects.

Common Mediterranean Herbs and Spices

While some of the spices in this book may be unfamiliar to you, most can be easily found in the herbs and spices section of a supermarket. For easy cooking, stock up on some of these dried essentials. Some come in whole or ground versions, so be sure to check the recipe to get the right kind.

Allspice
Basil
Bay leaves
Cardamom
Cayenne
Chives
Cinnamon
Clove
Coriander

Cumin
Fennel
Ginger
Marjoram
Nutmeg
Oregano
Paprika (sweet and smoked)
Parsley

Rosemary
Saffron
Sage
Sumac
Tarragon
Thyme
Turmeric

Turning Spices into Marinades

It's easy to make quick marinades out of your favourite spices. For 450g (1lb) meat or sliced vegetables, use 2 teaspoons ground spices (or a mixture of spices) and 2 tablespoons extra-virgin olive oil in a shallow container or resealable bag. Refrigerate while marinating for 2 to 24 hours. Because salt in marinades can make meat and vegetables soggy, wait to season until you're ready to cook.

SUMAC
This dried and ground fruit has a tart flavour that goes quite well with yogurt and lemon.

SAFFRON
This luxurious spice comes from a crocus flower and gives foods a very distinct golden hue.

TURMERIC
This rich yellow powder is made from dried rhizomes and has many health benefits, such as heartburn relief.

PAPRIKA
This crimson spice is made from ground chili peppers and can be smoked or sweet in flavour.

Mediterranean Spice Blends

The following are two common Mediterranean spice blends used often in this book. You can purchase them at most supermarkets or online.

Ras el hanout: This North African spice mixture contains an assortment of spices, often including cumin, clove, cinnamon, paprika, turmeric, cardamom, coriander, ginger, allspice, and black pepper.

Zahtar: This blend of spices often is used as a condiment and includes sesame, sumac, salt, thyme, oregano, and marjoram.

Salt

Salt gets a bad reputation for increasing blood pressure and leading to heart stress. While too much salt may have this effect, too little salt can also be detrimental. Natural sea salt (or sodium) is an essential electrolyte that can help with hydration. When consumed in moderation – around 1 to 2 teaspoons in total per day – it has been shown to be a beneficial and necessary part of a healthy diet.

Cooking with Fresh Herbs and Spices

Are you new to cooking with herbs and spices, or simply looking for new ways to cook with them? Here are some extra hints and tips:

- For the most flavour, **add dried herbs and spices at the beginning of cooking,** and leave fresh herbs for the end.

- Remember to **remove bay leaves, whole cinnamon sticks, allspice,** or **cloves** before serving.

- **Saffron stems are best when "bloomed"** in a tablespoon of warm water 5 to 20 minutes before being added (along with the residual water) to a recipe.

- Dried herbs and spices lose vibrancy and flavour on the shelf, and are **best if used within 6 months of purchase.**

Excellent with ripe tomatoes

Try with grilled prawn

BASIL

This pungent fresh herb has many varieties worldwide, with flavours ranging from sweet anise to lemon.

CARDAMOM

This warm and aromatic spice can be purchased ground or as small green pods full of whole seeds.

TARRAGON

Sold fresh or dried, this slender-leaf herb has a unique flavour and is often paired with chicken and fish.

CORIANDER

The dried seeds of the cilantro plant have a citrus flavour when ground and contain a significant amount of dietary fibre.

Spring and Summer
Meal Plan and Shopping List

	BREAKFAST	LUNCH	SNACK	DINNER	NEXT DAY PREP
SUNDAY	Asparagus and Spring Mushroom Omelette	Fig and Rocket Salad	Red pepper slices; almonds	Sole with Fresh Tomato Salad	Make Apricot and Pistachio Scones and Mojo Verde
MONDAY	Apricot and Pistachio Scones	Hemp Tabbouleh	Grilled Vegetables with Mojo Verde	Carrot Spirals with Carrot Top Pesto	
TUESDAY	Prawn and Harissa Frittata	Leftover Carrot Spirals with Carrot Top Pesto	Leftover Grilled Vegetables with Mojo Verde	Bouillabaisse	Make Gazpacho; begin Coconut Yogurt
WEDNESDAY	Leftover Apricot and Pistachio Scones	Leftover Hemp Tabbouleh	Gazpacho	Chicken Tagine with Apricots and Green Olives	
THURSDAY	Olive Oil-Fried Eggs; fresh strawberries	Leftover Chicken Tagine with Apricots and Green Olives	Leftover Gazpacho	Beef Kofta with Pine Nuts and Sumac; Balsamic Cucumbers with Dill	Make Nut and Seed Crackers and Olive and Preserved Lemon Tapenade
FRIDAY	Coconut Yogurt with Fresh Fruit	Leftover Beef Kofta with Pine Nuts and Sumac; Balsamic Cucumbers with Dill	Nut and Seed Crackers; Olive and Preserved Lemon Tapenade	Classic Greek Salad	Marinate chicken for Citrus-Grilled Chicken with Greens
SATURDAY	Paleo Crêpes with Lemon Curd	Citrus-Grilled Chicken with Greens	Leftover Nut and Seed Crackers and Olive and Preserved Lemon Tapenade	Tuna Steak with Orange and Fennel Salad	

The meal plan, opposite, provides one week of recipes for two adults, using fresh spring and summer ingredients. Below is a shopping list of everything you'll need.

VEGETABLES AND FRESH HERBS

25g (scant 1oz) fresh oregano
25g (scant 1oz) fresh tarragon
30g (1oz) fresh basil
50g (1¾oz) flat-leaf parsley
4 sprigs of dill
50g (1¾oz) fresh mint
20g (¾oz) fresh coriander
3 sprigs of thyme
240g (8¾oz) baby rocket (or use baby spinach)
1 small bunch frisee
1 large head romaine
575g (1¼lb) small to medium fennel bulbs
8 medium seasonal mushrooms
6 large cremini or white button mushrooms
340g (¾lb) asparagus spears
680g (1½lb) medium carrots (with greens)
4 medium red peppers
2 medium yellow peppers
1 jalapeño
1.25kg (2½lb) ripe heirloom or large tomatoes
4 medium tomatoes
14 cherry tomatoes
2 small Persian cucumbers
2 large English cucumbers
2 medium courgettes
1 medium head cauliflower
5cm (2in) piece fresh ginger root
4 small to medium leeks
1 small red onion
2 medium yellow onions
24 cloves garlic

DAIRY

2 tbsp chevre (optional)
115g (4oz) crumbled feta cheese (optional)
14 tbsp unsalted grass-fed butter (optional)

SEAFOOD, MEAT, AND EGGS

19 large eggs
2 x 110g (4oz) sole filets
2 x 110g (4oz) tuna steaks
225g (½ lb) halibut, cod, or another firm white fish
225g (½ lb) live mussels
450g (1lb) live small Manila or steamer clams
4 fresh scallops
340g (¾ lb) raw prawns
2 to 3 small anchovy fillets
680g (1½ lb) boneless, skinless chicken breasts
225g (½ lb) boneless, skinless chicken thighs
450g (1lb) lean ground beef

FRUITS

4 fresh figs (or use 8 dried)
285g (10 oz) fresh strawberries
2 medium oranges
1 medium lime
11 small lemons
140g (5oz) fresh fruit of choice
400g (14oz) dried apricots

NUTS AND SEEDS

15g (½oz) whole pecans
100g (3½oz) whole almonds
30g (1oz) blanched almonds
30g (1oz) shelled pistachios
200g (7oz) hazelnuts
6 tbsp toasted pine nuts
25g (1oz) raw sunflower seeds
45g (1½oz) raw pumpkin seeds
75g (2½oz) raw shelled hemp seeds
15g (½oz) flaxseeds
2 tbsp chia seeds
2 tbsp toasted sesame seeds
2 tsp whole caraway seeds
60g (2oz) nuts of choice

SPICES

Sea salt
Freshly ground black pepper
1 bay leaf
Ground cardamom
Cayenne pepper
Ground cinnamon
Ground cumin
Ground ginger
Freshly grated nutmeg
Smoked paprika (optional)
Crushed red pepper flakes
12 saffron threads
Sumac
Turmeric

DRY GOODS

1 litre (1¾ pints) extra-virgin olive oil
10 tbsp coconut oil or butter
60ml (2fl oz) balsamic vinegar
3 tbsp sherry vinegar
1 tsp harissa
1 tsp hot sauce (optional)
60g (2oz) pitted Castelvetrano olives
60g (2oz) pitted green olives
225g (8oz) pitted green or black olives
115g (4oz) pitted kalamata olives
2 preserved lemons (about 3 tbsp zest)
30g (1oz) sun-dried tomatoes
45g (1½ pints) artichoke hearts
2 tbsp coconut flour
375g (13oz) cups almond flour
125g (4½oz) tapioca flour
1 tsp baking soda
250ml (9fl oz) raw honey
5 (400ml; 14fl oz) cans full-fat coconut milk
2 probiotic acidophilus bifida gel capsules
850g (28 oz) canned, diced tomatoes
2 litres (3½ pints) fish or vegetable stock
120ml (4fl oz) chicken stock
115g (4oz) tomato juice
½ tsp Dijon mustard
1 tsp whole-grain mustard

Autumn and Winter
Meal Plan and Shopping List

	BREAKFAST	LUNCH	SNACK	DINNER	NEXT DAY PREP
SUNDAY	Courgette-Date Breakfast Bread	Leek and Celeriac Soup	Dried apricots; almonds	Garlic Ginger Prawns with Spiced Carrot-Currant Salad	Make dressing and seed pomegranate for Pomegranate and Fresh Herb Salad
MONDAY	Leftover Courgette-Date Breakfast Bread for Paleo French Toast; fresh berries	Pomegranate and Fresh Herb Salad	Leftover Leek and Celeriac Soup	Sweet Potato Pasta with Tomatoes and Meatballs	
TUESDAY	Tortilla Espagnole	Leftover Sweet Potato Pasta with Tomatoes and Meatballs	Fresh fruit; pecans	Soup alla Canavese; Olive and Onion Focaccia	Make Bay Prawn Cocktail Salad
WEDNESDAY	Leftover Tortilla Espagnole	Leftover Soup alla Canavese; Olive and Onion Focaccia	Bay Prawn Cocktail Salad	Salmon with Butternut Squash Couscous	Make Beetroot and Carrot Slaw; hard boil, chill, and peel 4 eggs
THURSDAY	Spiced Almond and Orange Porridge	Beetroot and Carrot Slaw with Tahini and Zahtar; hard-boiled eggs	Leftover Bay Prawn Cocktail Salad	Paprika-Rubbed Chicken with Broccolini	Make Green Zhug
FRIDAY	Leftover Spiced Almond and Orange Porridge	Leftover Paprika-Rubbed Chicken with Broccolini	Grain-Free Flatbread; Green Zhug	Cauliflower Steaks with Ras el Hanout; Roasted Carrots with Cumin and Yogurt	Make 2 extra Grain-Free Flatbreads to use in Fattoush
SATURDAY	Shakshuka	Fattoush	Leftover Green Zhug; vegetable slices	Coriander-Crusted Beef with Olive-Nut Tapenade; Braised Chard	

The meal plan, opposite, provides one week of recipes for two adults, using fresh autumn and winter ingredients. Below is a shopping list of everything you'll need.

VEGETABLES AND FRESH HERBS

4 bunches fresh coriander
30g (1oz) fresh mint
2 tbsp fresh basil
2 tbsp fresh basil, parsley, or dill
10g (¼oz) flat-leaf parsley
15g (½oz) fresh oregano
1 tsp fresh rosemary
85g (3oz) baby rocket
6 leaves lacinato kale
450g (1lb) Swiss chard
1 head romaine lettuce
2 medium courgettes
3 large heads cauliflower
350g (12oz) broccolini
2 medium radishes
5 large celery stalks
2 red peppers
1 yellow pepper
2 green Anaheim or jalapeño peppers
2 to 6 green serrano chillies
10 cherry tomatoes
1 medium tomato
2 small cucumbers
2 medium beetroots (with greens)
1.25kg (2½ lb) small carrots
11 medium carrots
2 medium sweet potatoes
1kg (2lb) celery root
4 medium cremini or white button mushrooms
1 (1kg; 2lb) butternut squash
7.5cm (3-in) piece fresh ginger root
1 small shallot
4 green onions
1 medium red onion
5 medium yellow onions
32 cloves garlic
115g (4oz) vegetable slices of choice

FRUITS

4 medium bananas
1 pomegranate
1 medium orange
4 medium lemons
140g (5oz) fresh berries
2 pieces fresh fruit of choice
4 large Medjool dates
225g (8oz) cup dried apricots
140g (5oz) dried currants

SEAFOOD, MEAT, AND EGGS

24 large eggs
340g (¾ lb) (about 16) raw prawns
450g (1lb) cooked prawns
2 (170g; 6oz) boneless salmon fillet slices
450g (1lb) ground chicken or turkey
2 whole chicken legs (680g; 1½ lb each)
55g (2oz) pancetta or bacon
2.25kg (5lb) beef chuck or shoulder roast

DAIRY

550g (20oz) full-fat Greek yogurt or coconut yogurt
1 tbsp unsalted grass-fed butter (optional)
60g (2oz) Parmigiano Reggiano cheese (optional)
60g (2oz) crumbled feta cheese (optional)

NUTS AND SEEDS

60g (2oz) walnuts
60g (2oz) whole almonds
85g (3oz) toasted hazelnuts
225g (8oz) shelled pistachios
1 cup pecans
2 tbsp whole flaxseeds
2 tbsp chia seeds
1 tbsp toasted sesame seeds
60g (2oz) raw nuts of choice

SPICES

Sea salt
Freshly ground black pepper
1 bay leaf
Ground cardamom
Cayenne pepper
Ground cloves
Whole coriander seeds
Ground cumin
Whole cumin seeds
Granulated garlic
Ground ginger
Italian seasoning
Onion flakes
Smoked paprika
Pumpkin pie spice
Ras el hanout
Red pepper flakes
Dried sage
Sumac
Zahtar

DRY GOODS

1 litre (1¾ pints) extra-virgin olive oil
500g (1lb 2oz) almond flour
30g (1oz) coconut flour
185g (6½oz) tapioca flour
2 tsp baking soda
90ml (3fl oz) raw honey
2 tsp apple cider vinegar
1 tbsp red wine vinegar
2 (400ml; 14fl oz) cans full-fat coconut milk
1 tsp pure vanilla extract
60ml (2fl oz) coconut oil
175g (6oz) pitted kalamata olives
200g (7oz) pitted green olives
½ preserved lemon (1 tbsp zest)
45g (1½oz) roasted red peppers
1 (800g; 28oz) can diced tomatoes
1 (800g; 28oz) can crushed tomatoes
3 tbsp tomato paste
1.25kg (2¾ lbs) chicken stock
250g (9oz) beef stock (optional)
3 tbsp tahini
1 tsp whole-grain mustard

breakfasts

What better way to start the day than with a Mediterranean Paleo meal? These recipes are packed full of natural vegetable fats, extra greens, and lean proteins. Whether you prefer a savoury or sweet breakfast, you'll find options to suit your style.

And because breakfast isn't always the best time to cook, you can even make many of these recipes ahead of time for quick eating on the go.

Fiery harissa, tamed with juicy ripe tomatoes and succulent prawns, pairs perfectly with a slightly bitter frisée salad in this breakfast frittata.

Prawn and Harissa
Frittata

10 MINUTES   **30 MINUTES**   **SERVES 2**

INGREDIENTS

3 large eggs

1 tsp harissa

2 tbsp flat-leaf parsley, chopped

¼ tsp freshly ground black pepper

2 tbsp extra virgin olive oil (or 1 tbsp unsalted butter and 1 tbsp extra virgin olive oil)

3 small garlic cloves, thinly sliced

60g (2oz) onion, finely diced

115g (¼lb) (about 8) raw prawns, shelled, deveined, and roughly chopped

6 cherry tomatoes, quartered

1 small bunch frisée, chopped

Juice of ½ medium lemon (about 1 tbsp)

Pinch sea salt (optional)

METHOD

1 Put the top oven rack on the second shelf from the top position (make sure there's enough room above to fit a cast-iron frying pan). Preheat the oven to 180°C (350°F).

2 In a small bowl, whisk together eggs, harissa, parsley, and black pepper. Set aside.

3 Heat a 15-cm (6-inch) cast-iron frying pan or oven-proof frying pan over medium-high heat. When the frying pan is hot, add 1 tablespoon olive oil and wait 30 seconds.

4 Add garlic and onion to the hot frying pan and sauté, stirring frequently, for 2 minutes, or until onion is slightly translucent.

5 Add prawns and cook, stirring frequently, until opaque and a bright pinkish-orange (about 30 seconds). Add cherry tomatoes and cook for another 30 seconds. Remove from heat.

6 Pour egg mixture evenly over top. Place the frying pan on the top rack of the oven.

7 Bake for 20 to 25 minutes, or until egg is set in the middle and a skewer inserted in the centre comes out clean.

8 Meanwhile, in a medium salad bowl, toss together frisée, remaining olive oil, and lemon juice. Add a pinch of sea salt and freshly ground black pepper, if desired. Divide onto plates.

9 Serve frittata warm or at room temperature with a side of dressed frisée.

EACH SERVING HAS:

Calories 319   Total Fat 23g   Carbohydrate 7g   Protein 22g

Velvety eggs are poached in a **fragrant hot pepper** and **tomato sauce**, and topped with **tangy feta crumbles** and **coriander**.

Shakshuka

15 MINUTES   **1 HOUR, 5 MINUTES**   **SERVES 4**

INGREDIENTS

2 tbsp extra virgin olive oil

1 medium onion, diced

3 garlic cloves, sliced

1 medium red or yellow pepper, deseeded and diced

2 jalapeño peppers, deseeded and diced

2 x 400g can crushed tomatoes, with juice

1 tsp paprika

½ tsp cayenne pepper

½ tsp ground cumin

½ tsp turmeric

2 tsp sea salt

350g (12oz) Swiss chard, kale, or spinach greens, roughly chopped

4 large eggs

handful of coriander, chopped

60g (2oz) crumbled feta cheese (optional)

METHOD

1 Heat a 3-litre (5¼-pints) casserole over medium-high heat. When the casserole is hot, add olive oil and wait 30 seconds.

2 Add onion and garlic, and sauté, stirring frequently, for 3 to 5 minutes, or until onion is translucent.

3 Add red pepper and peppers. Stir and cook for 3 minutes.

4 Add tomatoes (with juice), paprika, cayenne pepper, cumin, turmeric, sea salt, and Swiss chard. Stir with a wooden spoon until combined.

5 Cover, reduce heat to low, and continue to cook, stirring occasionally, for 30 minutes. Taste and add more sea salt, if desired.

6 Break each egg into a small glass bowl. Using a wooden spoon or ladle, carefully make 4 indentations in tomato-and-pepper mixture.

7 Slide each egg out of the bowl into an indentation. Cover immediately and cook for 18 to 20 minutes, or until eggs are cooked to desired doneness.

8 Garnish with coriander and feta cheese (if using) to serve.

Variation: This is a great recipe to use up any leftover cooked meat you might have on hand; chopped beef, lamb, or chorizo would all be excellent additions.

EACH SERVING HAS:

Calories **223**   Total Fat **14g**   Carbohydrate **16g**   Protein **11g**

This **light and fluffy omelette** is overflowing with **creamy leeks, earthy mushrooms,** and the **sweet anise flavour of fresh tarragon.**

Asparagus and Spring Mushroom Omelette

5 MINUTES   **15 MINUTES**   **SERVES 1**

INGREDIENTS

- 3 large eggs
- 2 tsp water
- ¼ tsp sea salt
- ⅛ tsp freshly ground black pepper
- 2 tbsp extra virgin olive oil (or 1 tbsp extra virgin olive oil and 1 tbsp unsalted butter)
- 1 small leek, white and light green parts only, thinly sliced
- 4 medium fresh mushrooms (any local variety)
- 115g (¼lb) asparagus, trimmed and sliced
- 2 tbsp tarragon, chopped

METHOD

1 In a medium bowl, whisk together eggs, water, sea salt, and black pepper for about 30 seconds, or until fully combined and slightly foamy. Set aside.

2 Place a medium non-stick frying pan over medium-high heat. Wait 30 seconds and add 1 tablespoon olive oil.

3 Add leek and mushrooms to hot oil. Sauté, stirring frequently, for 3 to 4 minutes, or until mushrooms soften and leek slices become translucent.

4 Add asparagus and continue to cook, stirring frequently, for 3 to 5 minutes, or until asparagus is bright green and slightly tender. Remove vegetables from the frying pan and set aside.

5 Reheat the frying pan over medium heat. Add remaining olive oil.

6 When the frying pan is hot, pour egg mixture into it. Shake the frying pan vigorously to spread egg evenly along the bottom.

7 As egg mixture begins to set up, use a rubber spatula to carefully lift cooked edges from the sides of the frying pan. Tilt the pan to allow raw egg to run down lifted edges towards the bottom of the frying pan to cook.

8 When egg mixture is firm, but still moist, place sautéed vegetables and fresh tarragon on one half. Using a wide plastic spatula, flip empty half of egg over top of vegetables. Cook for 1 minute, and slide onto a plate. Serve immediately.

Variation: In the autumn, replace asparagus with 1 small fennel bulb, sliced, and use chanterelle mushrooms to make a seasonally appropriate **Fennel and Chanterelle Omelette.**

EACH SERVING HAS:

Calories	Total Fat	Carbohydrate	Protein
507	44g	8g	23g

Classic fried eggs get a makeover with the exceptionally **fruity taste of high-quality olive oil** and are served over a bed of **peppery greens**.

Olive Oil-**Fried Eggs**

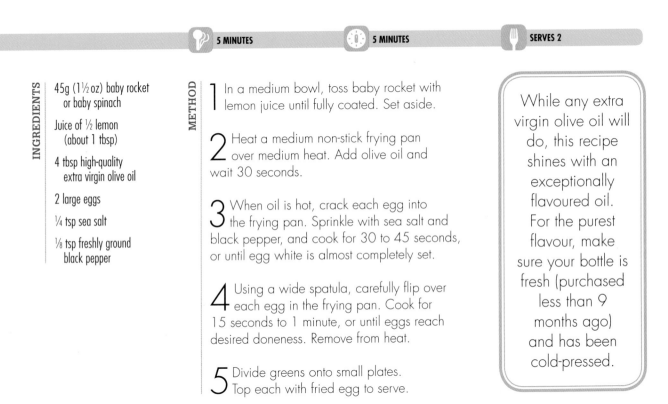

5 MINUTES   **5 MINUTES**   **SERVES 2**

INGREDIENTS

45g (1½ oz) baby rocket
or baby spinach

Juice of ½ lemon
(about 1 tbsp)

4 tbsp high-quality
extra virgin olive oil

2 large eggs

¼ tsp sea salt

⅛ tsp freshly ground
black pepper

METHOD

1 In a medium bowl, toss baby rocket with lemon juice until fully coated. Set aside.

2 Heat a medium non-stick frying pan over medium heat. Add olive oil and wait 30 seconds.

3 When oil is hot, crack each egg into the frying pan. Sprinkle with sea salt and black pepper, and cook for 30 to 45 seconds, or until egg white is almost completely set.

4 Using a wide spatula, carefully flip over each egg in the frying pan. Cook for 15 seconds to 1 minute, or until eggs reach desired doneness. Remove from heat.

5 Divide greens onto small plates. Top each with fried egg to serve.

While any extra virgin olive oil will do, this recipe shines with an exceptionally flavoured oil. For the purest flavour, make sure your bottle is fresh (purchased less than 9 months ago) and has been cold-pressed.

EACH SERVING HAS:

Calories **260**   Total Fat **26g**   Carbohydrate **3g**   Protein **7g**

This classic breakfast tortilla, brimming with **tender celery root slices,** is cooked in a base of **paprika-scented eggs** and garnished with **savoury spring onions.**

Tortilla Espagnole

15 MINUTES   **45 MINUTES**   **SERVES 4**

INGREDIENTS

¼ cup extra virgin olive oil

1 medium yellow onion, thinly sliced

2 garlic cloves, finely chopped

450g (1lb) celery root, peeled and cut into 1- to 2mm slices

1 tsp sea salt

¼ tsp freshly ground black pepper

½ tsp smoked paprika

8 large eggs, beaten

2 spring onions, white and light green parts only, thinly sliced

METHOD

1 Heat a 25- to 30cm (10- to 12-inch) cast-iron or ovenproof frying pan over medium heat. When the frying pan is hot, add olive oil and wait 30 seconds.

2 Add onion and garlic to the hot frying pan and sauté, stirring frequently, for 3 to 5 minutes, or until onion softens and becomes translucent.

3 Add celery root, sea salt, black pepper, and smoked paprika to the frying pan, and stir with a wooden spoon. Continue to cook, stirring every 5 minutes, for 15 to 20 minutes, or until celery root is tender when pierced with a fork. Taste and add more sea salt, if desired.

4 Spread celery root and onion evenly on the bottom of the frying pan. Pour beaten eggs over top of vegetable mixture and cook for about 1 minute. Reduce heat to low and continue to cook for 15 minutes, or until eggs are mostly set.

5 While eggs are cooking, turn the grill on high. Once eggs are mostly set, place the frying pan on the highest shelf in the oven. Grill for 5 minutes, or until eggs are completely set and tortilla is golden brown on top.

6 Serve warm, at room temperature, or chilled with sliced spring onions on top.

Variation: To make a **Chorizo and Piquillo Pepper Tortilla,** cook 115g (¼lb) ground chorizo along with onion, and add 3 thinly sliced piquillo peppers to vegetables after cooking.

EACH SERVING HAS:

Calories **338**   Total Fat **24g**   Carbohydrate **16g**   Protein **15g**

This toothsome bread combines **warm spices** with dates and **ripe bananas** for a breakfast that's every bit **as good as dessert.**

Courgette-Date
Breakfast Bread

	15 MINUTES		55 MINUTES		SERVES 8

INGREDIENTS

250g (9oz) almond flour

2 tbsp coconut flour

1 tsp baking soda

¼ tsp sea salt

1 tbsp pumpkin pie spice

4 large Medjool dates, pitted and chopped

2 medium bananas, peeled

3 large eggs

1 tsp apple cider vinegar

1 tsp pure vanilla extract

60ml (2fl oz) plus ½ tsp melted coconut oil

270g (9oz) shredded courgette

60g (2oz) walnuts, chopped

90ml (3fl oz) raw honey

METHOD

1 Preheat the oven to 170°C (325°F).

2 In a large bowl, combine almond flour, coconut flour, baking soda, sea salt, and pumpkin pie spice. Blend well with a fork until no lumps remain.

3 In a food processor, pulse dates, bananas, eggs, apple cider vinegar, vanilla extract, and 60ml (2fl oz) melted coconut oil for 1 to 2 minutes, or until puréed.

4 Pour date mixture into dry ingredients, along with shredded courgette and walnuts. Stir with a wooden spoon until completely combined.

5 Grease a 23x10cm (9x4in) loaf pan lightly with remaining melted coconut oil. Pour batter evenly into the pan. Bake for 45 to 55 minutes, or until a skewer inserted into the centre comes out clean.

6 Leave bread to cool before removing from the pan and slicing. Drizzle with raw honey to serve.

This bread makes an excellent base for Paleo French toast. Simply dip slices in beaten egg and fry in a lightly oiled pan, turning once, until egg has cooked through and is golden brown. Drizzle with grade-B maple syrup or raw honey, or top with fresh fruit, to serve.

EACH SERVING HAS:

Calories 385	Total Fat 28g	Carbohydrate 26g	Protein 11g

Tart and buttery lemon curd is a silky-smooth topping for crispy-edged, melt-in-your-mouth Paleo crêpes.

Paleo Crêpes with Lemon Curd

Lemon Curd

	2 HOURS, 10 MINUTES	15 MINUTES	SERVES 18

INGREDIENTS

3 large eggs

6 to 8 tbsp raw honey

120ml (4fl oz) lemon juice

1 tbsp lemon zest

¼ tsp sea salt

6 tbsp unsalted grass-fed butter, cut into cubes, or coconut oil

METHOD

1 Working over a small bowl or ramekin, carefully separate 1 egg, allowing white to fall into the bowl and yolk to stay in one half of shell. Place separated yolk in a separate medium bowl. Repeat with another egg.

2 Discard both whites from 2 eggs or refrigerate for use in omelettes or scrambled eggs another time. Add remaining egg (white and yolk) to yolks and whisk until fully incorporated. Set aside.

3 Place a small heavy-bottomed saucepan or steamer over medium-low heat. A steamer is best: you can make a steamer by placing a metal bowl over a saucepan, making sure there is about 5cm (2 inches) space between the bottom of the bowl and the bottom of the pan. Add 2.5cm (1 inch) water to the bottom pan before heating.

4 Add raw honey, lemon juice, lemon zest, and sea salt to the saucepan or top of the steamer. Whisk constantly and heat just until warmed (about 30°C [85°F]).

5 Remove from heat. Carefully pour about 30ml of lemon mixture into eggs, and quickly whisk to avoid scrambling eggs. While whisking, pour in another 30ml of lemon mixture. Continue until lemon mixture is fully incorporated into eggs.

6 Using a rubber spatula, return mixture to the pan and place over medium heat. Gradually add cubes of butter and stir constantly for 5 to 7 minutes, or until curd starts to thicken and tiny bubbles begin to surface. Remove from heat.

7 Strain curd through a mesh sieve or muslin into small jars. Chill in the fridge for 2 hours (curd should get thick as it cools). Serve with Paleo Crêpes.

EACH SERVING HAS:

Calories 105	Total Fat 7g	Carbohydrate 11g	Protein 2g

Paleo Crêpes

5 MINUTES | **12 MINUTES** | **SERVES 2**

INGREDIENTS

125g (4½oz) tapioca flour

240ml (8fl oz) coconut milk

1 large egg

¼ tsp sea salt

½ tsp coconut oil

METHOD

1 In a medium bowl, whisk flour, coconut milk, egg, and sea salt until fully incorporated. Set aside.

2 Heat a non-stick frying pan or griddle over medium heat. Grease the frying pan lightly with coconut oil.

3 When hot, pour ½ of batter onto the greased frying pan and cook for 2 to 3 minutes, or until little bubbles start to form on the surface.

4 Turn over crêpe and cook for 2 to 3 minutes, or until lightly browned. Repeat with rest of batter. Serve with 2 tbsp Lemon Curd.

EACH SERVING HAS:

Calories **445**   Total Fat **23g**   Carbohydrate **57g**   Protein **5g**

Aromatic **cardamom** and **clove** accent **rich almond flavours** in this citrus-heavy, warm breakfast cereal.

Spiced Almond and
Orange Porridge

🥄 **5 MINUTES**	⏱ **15 MINUTES**	🍴 **SERVES 6**

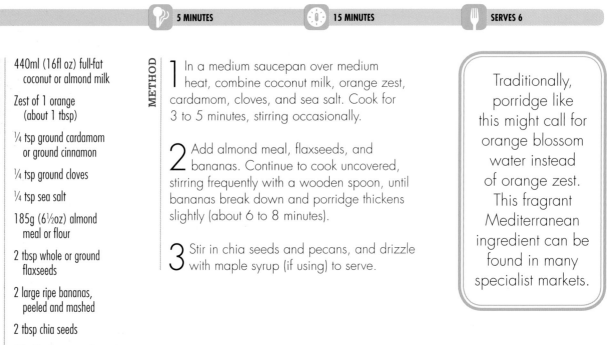

INGREDIENTS

440ml (16fl oz) full-fat coconut or almond milk

Zest of 1 orange (about 1 tbsp)

¼ tsp ground cardamom or ground cinnamon

¼ tsp ground cloves

¼ tsp sea salt

185g (6½oz) almond meal or flour

2 tbsp whole or ground flaxseeds

2 large ripe bananas, peeled and mashed

2 tbsp chia seeds

60g (2oz) pecans, chopped

Grade-B (number 2) pure maple syrup (optional)

METHOD

1 In a medium saucepan over medium heat, combine coconut milk, orange zest, cardamom, cloves, and sea salt. Cook for 3 to 5 minutes, stirring occasionally.

2 Add almond meal, flaxseeds, and bananas. Continue to cook uncovered, stirring frequently with a wooden spoon, until bananas break down and porridge thickens slightly (about 6 to 8 minutes).

3 Stir in chia seeds and pecans, and drizzle with maple syrup (if using) to serve.

> Traditionally, porridge like this might call for orange blossom water instead of orange zest. This fragrant Mediterranean ingredient can be found in many specialist markets.

EACH SERVING HAS:

Calories 471	Total Fat 38g	Carbohydrate 32g	Protein 10g

These crumbly scones are filled with **chewy dried apricots** and **crunchy pistachios,** brightened with a hint of **lemon, honey,** and **warm nutmeg.**

Apricot and Pistachio Scones

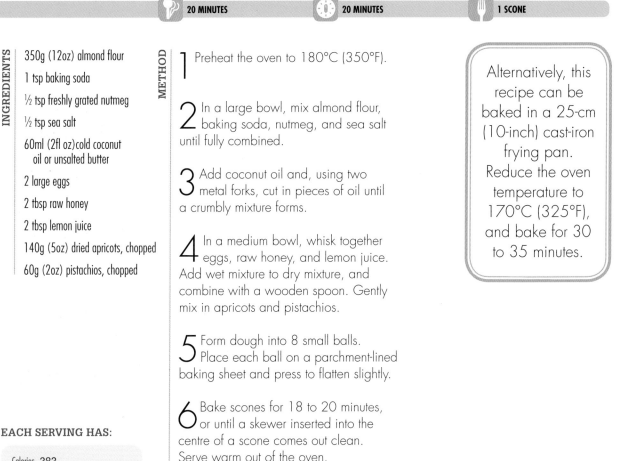

20 MINUTES · **20 MINUTES** · **1 SCONE**

INGREDIENTS

- 350g (12oz) almond flour
- 1 tsp baking soda
- ½ tsp freshly grated nutmeg
- ½ tsp sea salt
- 60ml (2fl oz) cold coconut oil or unsalted butter
- 2 large eggs
- 2 tbsp raw honey
- 2 tbsp lemon juice
- 140g (5oz) dried apricots, chopped
- 60g (2oz) pistachios, chopped

METHOD

1 Preheat the oven to 180°C (350°F).

2 In a large bowl, mix almond flour, baking soda, nutmeg, and sea salt until fully combined.

3 Add coconut oil and, using two metal forks, cut in pieces of oil until a crumbly mixture forms.

4 In a medium bowl, whisk together eggs, raw honey, and lemon juice. Add wet mixture to dry mixture, and combine with a wooden spoon. Gently mix in apricots and pistachios.

5 Form dough into 8 small balls. Place each ball on a parchment-lined baking sheet and press to flatten slightly.

6 Bake scones for 18 to 20 minutes, or until a skewer inserted into the centre of a scone comes out clean. Serve warm out of the oven.

Alternatively, this recipe can be baked in a 25-cm (10-inch) cast-iron frying pan. Reduce the oven temperature to 170°C (325°F), and bake for 30 to 35 minutes.

EACH SERVING HAS:

Calories **383**
Total Fat **29g**
Carbohydrate **22g**
Protein **11g**

Silky smooth and **tangy, to boot,** this Paleo yogurt is bound to become a **staple** in your Mediterranean kitchen.

Coconut Yogurt with Fresh Fruit

1 HOUR, 15 MINUTES **12 TO 24 HOURS** **115G (4OZ)**

INGREDIENTS

4 x 400ml cans full-fat coconut milk

2 probiotic acidophilus bifida gel capsules

Fresh seasonal fruit of choice

METHOD

1 Refrigerate coconut milk for at least 1 hour. When chilled, coconut milk should settle to the bottom of the can, with creamy coconut fat on top.

2 Carefully remove fat (coconut cream) from the top of each can and place in a sterilized one-litre (32fl oz) glass jam jar. Also add coconut milk from the bottom of each can. Discard remaining milk, or use for something else.

3 Break probiotic acidophilus bifida gel capsules and empty contents into the jar of coconut cream. Using a clean metal spoon, stir until probiotics and coconut cream are completely combined.

4 Place a sterilized lid on the jar and close tightly.

5 Wrap the jar with a large towel and place in a cooler with a heating pad set on low for 12 to 24 hours. Alternatively, place the jar in the oven with the door closed and the oven light on. Yogurt should stay between 40°C and 43°C (105°F and 110°F).

6 Yogurt will continue to get tangier the longer it sits. Chill before serving with fresh seasonal fruit.

To sterilize a glass jam jar, submerge the jar and lid in water. Place over high heat and boil for 5 minutes. Carefully remove the sterilized jar, and lid with tongs, and place on a clean towel. (Never place the hot jar on a cold surface, or it may break.)

EACH SERVING HAS:

Calories **169**
Total Fat **1g**
Carbohydrate **73g**
Protein **10g**

antipasto

Sometimes you just need a little pre-meal snack. These recipes are designed as starters, hors d'oeuvres, or small-portion snacks. Many are also excellent as party appetizer platters. And because no Mediterranean meal is complete without bread, I've also included a few grain-free options, along with several regional spreads.

Easy, chewy, and **delicious,** these quick Paleo flatbreads are a satisfying way to include **grain-free breads** in your day.

Grain-Free **Flatbread**

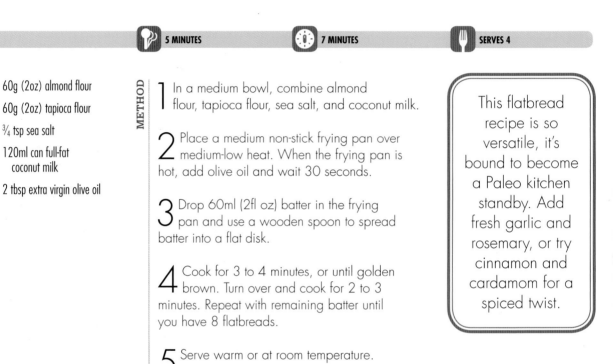

5 MINUTES   **7 MINUTES**   **SERVES 4**

INGREDIENTS

60g (2oz) almond flour

60g (2oz) tapioca flour

¾ tsp sea salt

120ml can full-fat
coconut milk

2 tbsp extra virgin olive oil

METHOD

1 In a medium bowl, combine almond flour, tapioca flour, sea salt, and coconut milk.

2 Place a medium non-stick frying pan over medium-low heat. When the frying pan is hot, add olive oil and wait 30 seconds.

3 Drop 60ml (2fl oz) batter in the frying pan and use a wooden spoon to spread batter into a flat disk.

4 Cook for 3 to 4 minutes, or until golden brown. Turn over and cook for 2 to 3 minutes. Repeat with remaining batter until you have 8 flatbreads.

5 Serve warm or at room temperature.

This flatbread recipe is so versatile, it's bound to become a Paleo kitchen standby. Add fresh garlic and rosemary, or try cinnamon and cardamom for a spiced twist.

EACH SERVING HAS:

Calories **237**   Total Fat **18g**   Carbohydrate **18g**   Protein **4g**

This **blazing-hot salsa** gets its intense flavour from **green serrano chillies**, **fresh garlic cloves**, and a **warm spice blend** of **cumin** and **cardamom**.

Green **Zhug**

10 MINUTES   **NONE**   **SERVES 8**

INGREDIENTS

2 bunches coriander (chopped)

2 to 6 green serrano chillies

4 garlic cloves

3 tbsp extra virgin olive oil

Juice of ½ lemon (about 1 tbsp)

1 tsp ground cumin

¼ tsp ground cardamom

½ tsp freshly ground black pepper

1 tsp sea salt

METHOD

1 Cut stems off coriander bunches. (Don't worry about stems remaining near leaves; just be sure to cut off bases.) Discard stems.

2 Slice stem tops off chillies and cut each in half. Remove seeds and white sections. Discard stems, seeds, and white membranes.

3 Place coriander leaves, chillies, garlic, olive oil, lemon juice, cumin, cardamom, black pepper, and sea salt in a food processor.

4 Blend on high for 30 seconds, or until a chunky, salsa-like consistency is formed. Adjust salt, if needed.

5 Serve as a spread with Grain-Free Flatbread or crackers.

Variation: To make **Red Zhug,** simply use red serranos instead of green, and add ⅛ teaspoon ground cloves. Fully ripened red serranos are often hotter than the unripened green variety, so you may want to use a few less in this recipe.

Chilli oils and fumes can burn, so it's a good idea to wear disposable or rubber kitchen gloves when handling them. Wash your hands thoroughly with soap and warm water afterwards to get rid of any oils, and try not to touch your eyes or face right after handling.

EACH SERVING HAS:

Calories 54	Total Fat 5g	Carbohydrate 2g	Protein 0g

Smoky paprika, nutty-roasted cauliflower, and sweet red peppers combine to make the perfect pre-party Paleo snack.

Roasted Red Pepper **Hummus**

15 MINUTES   **30 MINUTES**   **SERVES 8**

INGREDIENTS

1 large cauliflower, cut into florets

5 garlic cloves

2 tbsp extra virgin olive oil

½ tsp ground cumin

60g (2oz) roasted red peppers or piquillo peppers, chopped

½ cup tahini

Juice of 1 lemon (about 2 tbsp)

½ tsp sea salt

¼ tsp smoked paprika

METHOD

1 Preheat the oven to 180°C (350°F).

2 On a large baking tray, spread cauliflower florets and garlic. Drizzle with olive oil and sprinkle with cumin.

3 Bake for 25 to 30 minutes, or until cauliflower is tender, stirring with a wooden spoon every 10 to 15 minutes. Remove from the oven.

4 Scrape warm cauliflower and garlic into a food processor fitted with a chopping blade. Add red peppers, tahini, lemon juice, sea salt, and smoked paprika.

5 Process to a smooth consistency. Taste; adjust sea salt and lemon juice, if desired.

6 Serve warm or chilled with Paleo crackers or vegetable slices.

You can find roasted red peppers in a jar in most grocery stores, and cans of tangy Spanish piquillo peppers can be found at many specialist markets. Note that many canned piquillo peppers have added sugar, so you may wish to leave them out for that reason.

EACH SERVING HAS:

Calories **132**   Total Fat **10g**   Carbohydrate **9g**   Protein **5g**

Chewy, salty focaccia is topped with **kalamata olives, fresh rosemary,** and **crispy onion flakes.** This **grain-free** bread is just as delicious as the original!

Olive and Onion **Focaccia**

10 MINUTES   **20 MINUTES**   **SERVES 8**

INGREDIENTS

125g (4½oz) tapioca flour

2 tbsp coconut flour

2 tsp sea salt

½ tsp baking soda

3 large eggs

60ml can full-fat coconut milk or cream

½ tsp apple cider vinegar

6 tbsp, plus ½ tsp extra virgin olive oil

1 tbsp onion flakes

1 tsp fresh rosemary, chopped

30g (1oz) kalamata olives, pitted and halved

METHOD

1 Preheat the oven to 190°C (375°F).

2 In a medium bowl, combine tapioca flour, coconut flour, 1 teaspoon sea salt, and baking soda. Mix with a fork or sift to remove any lumps. Set aside.

3 In a stand mixer, beat eggs, coconut milk, apple cider vinegar, and 4 tablespoons olive oil. Add dry ingredients and beat until fully incorporated.

4 Lightly grease a 23-cm (9-inch) square baking pan or 25-cm (10-inch) cast-iron frying pan with ½ teaspoon olive oil. Pour batter into the pan.

5 Sprinkle onion flakes and rosemary over batter, and place kalamata olives evenly on top.

6 Bake for 16 to 20 minutes, or until a skewer inserted in middle of focaccia comes out clean.

7 Immediately brush remaining olive oil over bread, and sprinkle with remaining sea salt. Serve warm.

Variation: To make **Sun-Dried Tomato Basil Focaccia,** eliminate onion flakes, rosemary, and kalamata olives, and replace with 15g (½oz) chopped sun-dried tomatoes, 1 teaspoon granulated garlic, and 3 large, fresh basil leaves, thinly sliced.

EACH SERVING HAS:

Calories	Total Fat	Carbohydrate	Protein
214	16g	16g	3g

Pungent garlic and **sweet, ripe tomatoes,** accentuated with nothing more than **olive oil** and **sea salt,** make this simple spread shine.

Fresh Tomato and Garlic
Spread

| 10 MINUTES | 15 MINUTES | SERVES 12 |

INGREDIENTS

6 large tomatoes
(about 1kg; 2lb)

4 garlic cloves, finely chopped

2 tbsp extra virgin olive oil

½ tsp sea salt

This spread is excellent as a topping for fish or chicken. It can also be used as a marinade for meat, cheese, or vegetables.

METHOD

1 Fill a 7 to 8¾-pint (4 to 5-litre) saucepan with 5¼ pints (3 litres) of water. Cover and place over high heat until water comes to the boil (large bubbles breaking on the surface).

2 Meanwhile, using a small paring knife, carefully score an "X" on the bottom of each tomato. Make sure to cut just through skin and not into flesh of tomato.

3 While waiting for water to boil, fill a large bowl with iced water and set it next to the stove, along with a slotted spoon or skimmer.

4 When water comes to the boil, carefully drop tomatoes into the pot (being careful hot water doesn't splash out). Cook for 45 to 60 seconds, or until skins wrinkle slightly.

5 Using the slotted spoon, remove cooked tomatoes from boiling water and plunge immediately into iced water.

6 When tomatoes have cooled, remove from iced water. Carefully peel skins off each tomato, starting with skin next to the "X." Discard skins. Cut each tomato in half.

7 Place peeled tomato halves into a food processor fitted with a chopping blade. Add garlic, olive oil, and sea salt, and process on high for 30 to 45 seconds, or until puréed. Adjust sea salt, if desired.

8 Serve alongside bread or crackers.

EACH SERVING HAS:

| Calories 35 | Total Fat 2g | Carbohydrate 3g | Protein 1g |

This pungent spread combines **briny olives** and **anchovy fillets** with the unmistakable **flavour of preserved lemon.**

Olive and Preserved Lemon
Tapenade

5 MINUTES   **NONE**   **SERVES 8**

INGREDIENTS

1 preserved lemon, seeds removed but rind intact

430g (15oz) green or black olives, pitted

2 to 3 anchovy fillets, chopped

30g (1oz) flat-leaf parsley, chopped

2 tbsp extra virgin olive oil

¼ tsp freshly ground black pepper

¼ tsp crushed red pepper flakes

30g (1oz) toasted almonds, coarsely chopped (optional)

METHOD

1 Cut preserved lemon into thin slices (you'll need about 2 tablespoons).

2 In a food processor, pulse preserved lemon slices, green olives, anchovy fillets, parsley, olive oil, black pepper, crushed red pepper flakes, and almonds (if using) until a coarse mixture forms, or about 15 to 30 seconds.

3 Serve at room temperature or chilled, with crackers or fresh vegetable slices.

Preserved lemons are whole lemons that have been packed in salt – releasing their natural juices to make a preserving solution – and stored for a minimum of 3 weeks to fully preserve. They can be found at most high-end delicatessens and grocery shops.

EACH SERVING HAS:

Calories	Total Fat	Carbohydrate	Protein
153	15g	5g	3g

Crispy, **nutty,** and **delicious,** these Paleo crackers are sure to please even the pickiest eaters.

Nut and Seed Crackers

20 MINUTES   **20 MINUTES**   **SERVES 10**

INGREDIENTS

140g (5oz) raw whole almonds

115g (4oz) raw whole hazelnuts

60g (2oz) raw pumpkin seeds

75g (2½ oz) raw sunflower seeds

60g (2oz) flaxseeds

2 tbsp chia seeds

2 tbsp toasted sesame seeds (white or black)

2 tsp whole caraway seeds

2 large eggs, slightly beaten

2 tbsp coconut flour, for forming crackers (optional)

½ tsp sea salt

METHOD

1 Preheat the oven to 180°C (350°F).

2 In a food processor, pulse almonds, hazelnuts, pumpkin seeds, sunflower seeds, and flaxseeds for 30 seconds to 1 minute, or until a course meal forms. Remove from the processor and place in a medium bowl.

3 Add chia seeds, sesame seeds, and caraway seeds, and mix with a wooden spoon until fully combined. Add eggs and continue to stir until mixture forms a slightly sticky dough.

4 Cut 2 pieces of parchment paper to fit the bottoms of 2 large baking sheets (or use silicone sheet liners).

5 Form dough into 2.5-cm (1-inch) balls. Place balls at least 15cm (6in) apart on baking sheets.

6 Using a 600ml (20fl oz) jam jar or flat-bottomed glass, press balls into thin, disc-like crackers. (It may be helpful to press the jar or glass into coconut flour between pressings to keep dough from sticking to the glass.)

7 Sprinkle each cracker with sea salt. Bake for 15 to 20 minutes, or until lightly browned and crispy around the edges. Remove from the oven and rest for 10 minutes.

8 Using a spatula, carefully remove crackers from the sheets and leave to cool completely on a wire rack before storing in an airtight container. Repeat steps 4 through 8 with any remaining dough.

Variation: To make **Garlic Rosemary Crackers,** add 1 teaspoon granulated garlic and 2 tablespoons fresh rosemary, finely chopped, to dough.

EACH SERVING HAS:

Calories	Total Fat	Carbohydrate	Protein
218	18g	9g	8g

Smoky grilled vegetables are slathered with an **aromatic sauce of jalapeño, garlic,** and **coriander.**

Grilled Vegetables with
Mojo Verde

10 MINUTES · **5 MINUTES** · **SERVES 6**

INGREDIENTS

2 medium courgette, trimmed

2 medium red peppers, deseeded and quartered

2 medium yellow peppers, deseeded and quartered

4 to 6 asparagus spears, trimmed

6 large cremini or white button mushrooms, halved

6 tbsp extra virgin olive oil

½ tsp smoked paprika (optional)

1 jalapeño pepper, deseeded

3 garlic cloves, crushed

15g (½oz) coriander, chopped

60g (2oz) flat-leaf parsley, chopped

½ tsp sea salt

METHOD

1 Preheat the grill to high.

2 Cut each courgette in half lengthways. Cut each half lengthways again to make long, spear-like quarters.

3 In a large shallow dish or mixing bowl, combine courgette, red peppers, yellow peppers, asparagus, cremini mushrooms, 2 tablespoons olive oil, and smoked paprika (if using), and toss until vegetables are fully coated. Set aside.

4 In a food processor, combine remaining olive oil, jalapeño, garlic, coriander, parsley, and sea salt. Pulse for about 1 minute, or until puréed. Add more olive oil or sea salt, if desired. Place in a small serving bowl and set aside.

5 Place vegetables on the grill. Use a grill pan, if desired, or simply place longer vegetables crosswise against the grates to make sure they don't fall through. Grill for 1 to 2 minutes. Turn over and cook for 1 to 2 more minutes.

6 Remove from the grill. Serve roasted vegetables warm or chilled alongside Mojo Verde.

EACH SERVING HAS:

| Calories 129 | Total Fat 11g | Carbohydrate 8g | Protein 3g |

Buttery salmon with **tart capers** and **herbaceous fresh dill** form **flaky little cakes** fancy enough for any special occasion, but easy enough for an everyday meal.

Salmon Cakes with Capers and Dill

10 MINUTES   **5 MINUTES**   **SERVES 6**

INGREDIENTS

340g (¾lb) skinless salmon fillets, bones removed

1 large egg

1 tbsp coconut flour

½ tsp sea salt

1 tbsp capers

1 tbsp dill, finely chopped

2 tbsp extra virgin olive oil

METHOD

1 Cut salmon fillets into 4 slices each. In a food processor, pulse salmon fillets for 15 to 20 seconds, or until roughly chopped.

2 In a medium bowl, whisk egg, coconut flour, and sea salt. Add salmon, capers, and dill, and stir with a wooden spoon until fully combined.

3 Heat a medium frying pan over medium-high heat. When the pan is hot, add olive oil and wait 30 seconds.

4 Carefully drop a spoonful of salmon mixture into the hot frying pan; it should sizzle. Drop remaining batter into the pan until you have 6 cakes, spacing each spoonful at least 5cm (2 inches) apart.

5 Cook for 1 to 2 minutes, or until golden brown. Turn over each cake and press down lightly. Cook for 1 to 2 minutes, or until cakes are cooked through and golden brown.

6 Remove cakes from the hot frying pan and place on kitchen paper to absorb any extra oil. Serve immediately.

These cakes are excellent topped with garlicky alioli or creamy tzatziki.

EACH SERVING HAS:

Calories **170**   Total Fat **13g**   Carbohydrate **1g**   Protein **12g**

Tiny **bay prawns** steal the show in this cocktail salad with **toasty red peppers,** a **splash of lemon,** and a medley of **verdant fresh herbs.**

Bay Prawn Cocktail Salad

10 MINUTES | **NONE** | **SERVES 4**

INGREDIENTS

2 tbsp flat-leaf parsley, chopped

2 tbsp mint, chopped

2 tbsp basil, chopped

2 tsp extra virgin olive oil

Juice of ½ lemon
(about 1 tbsp)

450g (1lb) cooked
prawns

45g (1½ oz) roasted red
peppers, sliced into
3mm (⅛-in) strips

¼ tsp sea salt, or to taste

⅛ tsp freshly ground
black pepper

METHOD

1 In a medium bowl, combine parsley, mint, basil, olive oil, and lemon juice.

2 Add prawns and roasted red peppers, and stir with a wooden spoon until combined.

3 Add sea salt and black pepper, stir, and taste. Add more sea salt, if desired. Serve or refrigerate immediately.

This salad will keep nicely in the fridge for up to 24 hours. Most seafood gets mushy and odorous if kept longer than that.

EACH SERVING HAS:

Calories	Total Fat	Carbohydrate	Protein
140	4g	2g	24g

Piquant **Spanish-style chorizo** and **candy-like Medjool dates** pair perfectly in these snappy little treats, drizzled with **peppery Aleppo honey.**

Chorizo-Stuffed Dates
with Aleppo Honey

15 MINUTES   **25 MINUTES**   **SERVES 8**

INGREDIENTS

42g (1½oz) hard Spanish-style chorizo

16 large Medjool dates, pitted

8 thin slices bacon, cut in half

2 tbsp raw honey

½ tsp ground Aleppo pepper or sweet paprika

METHOD

1 Preheat the oven to 190°C (375°F).

2 Cut a piece of parchment paper to line the bottom of a large baking tray (or use a silicone sheet liner).

3 Cut chorizo into 16 pieces, each about 2.5x.5x.5cm (1 x ¼ x ¼ inch).

4 Stuff each date with 1 chorizo piece, and wrap ½ bacon slice around each date. To secure, skewer the dates in pairs with toothpicks. Place wrapped dates on the baking tray.

5 Bake for 15 minutes. Remove the baking tray from the oven and carefully turn over each date.

6 Return to the oven and bake for 8 to 10 minutes, or until bacon is cooked through and crisp on top.

7 Meanwhile, in a small bowl, combine raw honey and Aleppo pepper. Drizzle over dates to serve.

Variation: If you want to avoid pork products, you can easily make **Manchego and Marcona Almond–Stuffed Dates** by substituting pieces of hard Manchego cheese for chorizo and stuffing a whole Marcona almond with cheese inside of each date. Skip wrapping each date in bacon, and instead bake for 4 minutes on each side.

EACH SERVING HAS:

| Calories 205 | Total Fat 4g | Carbohydrate 41g | Protein 5g |

salads

Salads are the axle of the Mediterranean Paleo diet wheel. This chapter includes loads of meals starring fresh, in-season produce, herbs, and home-made olive oil dressings. From simple to spectacular, you have choices for every season and occasion.

While many of these recipes don't include meat, you can always add a small portion of lean protein if you need it. Remember, however, fresh vegetables should make up the majority of these salads.

In this salad, **juicy ripe watermelon** and **sweet red onion** are doused in a mixture of **refreshing herbs, olive oil,** and **tangy feta cheese.**

Fresh Watermelon Salad

15 MINUTES   NONE   SERVES 4

INGREDIENTS

1 small seedless watermelon (about 2.25kg/5 lb)

20 large mint leaves, chopped

10 large basil leaves, chopped

15g (½ oz) flat-leaf parsley, chopped

4 (1- to 2mm-thick) slices red onion, separated into rings

2 tbsp extra virgin olive oil

1 tbsp pistachios, shelled and chopped

¼ tsp coarse sea salt

60g (2oz) crumbled feta cheese (optional)

METHOD

1 Using a large chef's knife, carefully slice watermelon in half. Place flat side down and slice both halves into 2.5-cm (1-inch) thick slices.

2 Trim rind (including all green and white portions) and discard. Cut melon into 2.5x2.5cm (1x1-inch) cubes.

3 In a large salad bowl, combine watermelon cubes, mint leaves, basil leaves, flat-leaf parsley, and red onion.

4 Drizzle with olive oil and sprinkle with pistachios, sea salt, and crumbled feta cheese (if using). Serve immediately.

You can use whatever fresh herbs you have on hand for this recipe. Feel free to use coriander, chives, dill, oregano, or a combination!

EACH SERVING HAS:

| Calories 217 | Total Fat 13g | Carbohydrate 18g | Protein 6g |

Fattoush is a classic Lebanese salad of **toasted flatbread, crisp radishes,** cucumber, mint, and a **punchy lemon-garlic vinaigrette** with **tart sumac.**

Fattoush

10 MINUTES | **20 MINUTES** | **SERVES 2**

INGREDIENTS

1 or 2 Grain-Free Flatbreads or pittas

2 tbsp extra virgin olive oil

1 tbsp lemon juice

1 garlic clove, finely chopped

3 tbsp mint, finely chopped

2 tsp sumac

¼ tsp sea salt

2 medium radishes, trimmed and thinly sliced

1 medium tomato, diced

1 small cucumber, thinly sliced

2 spring onions, sliced

1 head romaine lettuce, thinly sliced or shredded

METHOD

1 Preheat the oven to 180°C (350°F).

2 Cut Grain-Free Flatbreads into 2.5cm (1-inch) strips. Place strips on a metal baking sheet. Bake for 15 to 20 minutes, or until browned and crispy.

3 Meanwhile, in a small bowl, whisk olive oil, lemon juice, garlic, mint, sumac, and sea salt until fully combined to make dressing. Alternatively, place ingredients into a small jam jar, cover tightly with a lid, and shake vigorously until fully combined.

4 Break up toasted flatbread strips into smaller sections.

5 In a large bowl, toss toasted flatbread pieces, dressing, radishes, tomato, cucumber, spring onions, and romaine lettuce until coated. Serve immediately.

Sumac has a slightly tangy, bitter taste and adds a unique flavour that's hard to replicate. Ground sumac can be found in many specialist shops or online through a variety of suppliers.

EACH SERVING HAS:

| Calories 484 | Total Fat 34g | Carbohydrate 40g | Protein 10g |

Jewels of **pomegranate** perch on top of a bed of **peppery rocket** and **juicy tomatoes**, drizzled with a **sweet** and **pungent ras el hanout dressing.**

Pomegranate and
Fresh Herb Salad

| | 15 MINUTES | | NONE | | SERVES 2 |

INGREDIENTS

1 ripe pomegranate

Juice of ½ lemon
(about 1 tbsp)

1 tsp raw honey

2 tbsp extra virgin olive oil

1 tsp ras el hanout

¼ tsp sea salt (optional)

85g (3oz) baby rocket

½ small shallot, thinly
sliced or shaved

10 cherry tomatoes,
quartered

handful of mint
leaves, chopped

handful of coriander,
chopped

60g (2oz) shelled and
toasted pistachios

METHOD

1 Put on an apron to protect clothing. Fill a large bowl with water, leaving 5cm (2 inches) from top of water to the top of the bowl.

2 Using a sharp knife, carefully cut pomegranate in half and place both halves into water. Immediately wipe up any juice on the cutting board to prevent staining.

3 Keeping pomegranate fully submerged, carefully tear each half apart, separating red seeds from white pith and rind. Discard pith and rind.

4 Using a medium colander or mesh strainer, strain seeds from water. Discard water and return drained seeds to the bowl. Remove any remaining white pith. Set aside.

5 In a small bowl, whisk lemon juice, raw honey, olive oil, ras el hanout, and sea salt (if using) until fully combined to make dressing. Alternatively, place ingredients into a small jam jar, cover tightly with a lid, and shake vigorously until fully combined.

6 Add baby rocket, shallot, cherry tomatoes, mint, coriander, and dressing to pomegranate seeds. Toss to coat. Top with toasted pistachios and serve immediately.

EACH SERVING HAS:

| Calories | 405 | Total Fat | 29g | Carbohydrate | 34g | Protein | 10g |

Hemp seeds make the perfect Paleo base for this **Mediterranean salad**, tossed with **parsley, mint, tomato, cucumber,** and a hearty dose of **garlic** and **lemon**.

Hemp **Tabbouleh**

40 MINUTES   **NONE**   **SERVES 4**

INGREDIENTS

- 30g (1oz) flat-leaf parsley, chopped
- 30g (1oz) mint, chopped
- 2 garlic cloves, finely chopped
- 4 medium tomatoes, diced
- 1 small Persian cucumber or ½ English cucumber, diced
- 240g (8½ oz) raw shelled hemp seeds
- Juice of 1 lemon (about 2 tbsp)
- 3 tbsp extra virgin olive oil
- ½ tsp sea salt

METHOD

1 In a large bowl, combine parsley, mint, garlic, tomatoes, Persian cucumber, hemp seeds, lemon juice, olive oil, and sea salt.

2 Taste and add more lemon juice or sea salt, if desired. Chill for 30 minutes before serving.

Usually tabbouleh is made with bulgur wheat. Instead, this version calls for raw hemp seeds. Also called *hemp hearts*, these seeds are nutritional powerhouses loaded with protein, fibre, and omega-3 fatty acids.

EACH SERVING HAS:

| Calories 513 | Total Fat 43g | Carbohydrate 16g | Protein 23g |

This quick pickle recipe uses **crisp English cucumbers, tangy balsamic vinegar,** and **fresh dill** to create a refreshing side salad.

Balsamic Cucumbers
with Dill

15 MINUTES TO 12 HOURS	**NONE**	**SERVES 4**

INGREDIENTS

1 large English cucumber, ends trimmed

½ tsp sea salt

2 tbsp balsamic vinegar

2 tsp extra virgin olive oil

2 tbsp dill, chopped

METHOD

1 Carefully cut English cucumber into 1- to 2mm slices.

2 Place cucumber slices in a medium bowl. Add sea salt, balsamic vinegar, olive oil, and fresh dill, and stir to combine completely.

3 Leave to stand for 10 minutes, or cover and refrigerate for up to 12 hours. Stir again before serving.

Variation: This recipe is fantastic savoury or sweet. To make **Balsamic Strawberries with Fresh Mint,** replace cucumber with 450g (1lb) sliced strawberries, eliminate sea salt, and replace dill with fresh mint.

You can use 2 to 3 small Persian cucumbers in this salad as well, or any small, tender pickling cucumber. If you can find only traditional cucumbers at the supermarket, you may want to peel off the tougher skins before slicing.

EACH SERVING HAS:

Calories 49	Total Fat 2g	Carbohydrate 7g	Protein 1g

Tender **pea shoots** and **sweet asparagus** star in this spring salad, adorned with crisp **radishes**, a bit of heat from a **Calabrian chilli,** and **toasted hazelnuts.**

Pea Shoots with
Asparagus and Radishes

15 MINUTES   **NONE**   **SERVES 2**

INGREDIENTS

- 2 tbsp extra virgin olive oil
- Juice of ½ medium lemon (about 1 tbsp)
- ¼ tsp sea salt
- ⅛ tsp freshly ground black pepper
- 510g (1lb 2oz) fresh pea shoots (tender parts only)
- 8 medium asparagus spears, trimmed and sliced into 2.5cm (1-in) pieces
- 6 medium radishes, trimmed and quartered
- 85g (3oz) sugar snap peas, sliced in half
- 2 spring onions, thinly sliced
- 1 small Calabrian chilli, diced, or ½ tsp crushed red pepper flakes
- 60g (2oz) toasted hazelnuts, coarsely chopped

METHOD

1 In a small bowl, whisk olive oil, lemon juice, sea salt, and black pepper until fully combined to make dressing. Alternatively, place ingredients into a small jam jar, cover tightly with a lid, and shake vigorously until fully combined.

2 In a large salad bowl, combine pea shoots, asparagus, radishes, sugar snap peas, spring onions, Calabrian chilli, and dressing. Toss until vegetables are fully coated.

3 Top with toasted hazelnuts and serve immediately.

This recipe is best saved for the spring season, when fresh pea shoots are tender and sweet. Use baby spinach as an excellent alternative any other time of the year.

EACH SERVING HAS:

Calories	Total Fat	Carbohydrate	Protein
405	32g	25g	11g

This briny salad from Provence gets its flavour from **traditional niçoise olives, hearty tuna,** and a **zippy anchovy vinaigrette.**

Niçoise Salad

| 10 MINUTES | 20 MINUTES | SERVES 2 |

INGREDIENTS

3 large eggs

6 small Jerusalem artichokes, peeled and halved

10 green beans or haricots verts, trimmed

2 tbsp extra virgin olive oil

1 tsp white wine vinegar

1 tsp Dijon mustard

¼ tsp freshly ground black pepper

4 anchovies, finely chopped

1 tbsp chives, chopped

1 butterhead lettuce, chopped

8 cherry tomatoes, halved

60g (2oz) niçoise olives, pitted

1 (140g; 5-oz) can oil-packed albacore or yellowfin tuna, drained

METHOD

1 Place eggs in a small saucepan and cover with cold water. Place on high heat until water begins to simmer. Immediately remove the pan from heat, cover, and set a kitchen timer for 13 minutes.

2 When the timer sounds, carefully remove eggs and plunge in cold water until cooled. Remove eggs from shells and cut into quarters.

3 Meanwhile, place artichokes in a second medium pan, with 1 litre (1¾ pints) water. Place the pan on high heat, covered, until water begins to simmer.

4 Reduce heat to medium and continue to cook artichokes for 4 to 6 minutes, or until slightly tender. Add green beans and cook for 30 more seconds. Strain vegetables and immediately submerge in cold water until cooled.

5 In a small bowl, whisk olive oil, white wine vinegar, mustard, and black pepper until fully combined to make dressing. Alternatively, place ingredients into a small jam jar, cover tightly with a lid, and shake vigorously until fully combined. Add anchovies and chives, and stir (or shake) again.

6 In a large salad bowl, combine lettuce, cooled artichokes and green beans, cherry tomatoes, olives, and dressing.

7 Toss until vegetables are fully coated with dressing. Top with tuna and hard-boiled egg quarters to serve.

EACH SERVING HAS:

| Calories 564 | Total Fat 40g | Carbohydrate 10g | Protein 31g |

This salad uses **crisp romaine lettuce** with a traditional combination of **sharp red onion, cool cucumber, tangy feta,** and **lemon Dijon dressing.**

Classic Greek Salad

15 MINUTES   **NONE**   **SERVES 2**

INGREDIENTS

2 tbsp extra virgin olive oil

Juice of ½ lemon
(about 1 tbsp)

1 garlic clove, finely chopped

½ tsp Dijon mustard

¼ tsp sea salt

¼ tsp freshly ground
black pepper

1 large head romaine
lettuce, chopped

8 cherry tomatoes, halved

4 red onion slices, halved

1 small cucumber, diced

60g (2oz) kalamata olives,
pitted and halved

125g (4½ oz) crumbled feta
cheese (optional)

METHOD

1 In a small bowl, whisk olive oil, lemon juice, garlic, mustard, sea salt, and black pepper until fully combined to make dressing. Alternatively, place ingredients into a small jam jar, cover tightly with a lid, and shake vigorously until fully combined.

2 In a large bowl, toss romaine lettuce, cherry tomatoes, red onion slices, cucumber, and dressing until vegetables are fully coated.

3 Top with olives and crumbled feta cheese (if using) to serve.

If you want a bit more protein in this meal, you can easily grill and slice a few boneless, skinless chicken breasts to add on top.

EACH SERVING HAS:

| Calories 413 | Total Fat 32g | Carbohydrate 28g | Protein 8g |

Luscious fresh figs steal the show in this easy salad, accented with the sweet flavour of **balsamic vinegar** and tossed with **peppery rocket** and **pecans**.

Fig and Rocket Salad

10 MINUTES   **NONE**   **SERVES 2**

INGREDIENTS

2 tbsp extra virgin olive oil

2 tbsp balsamic vinegar

¼ tsp sea salt

¼ tsp freshly ground black pepper

85g (3oz) rocket

4 fresh figs, quartered

30g (1oz) pecans, chopped

2 tbsp chèvre (optional)

METHOD

1 In a small bowl, whisk olive oil, balsamic vinegar, sea salt, and black pepper until fully combined to make dressing. Alternatively, place ingredients into a small jam jar, cover tightly with a lid, and shake vigorously until fully combined.

2 In a large bowl, combine rocket, figs, pecans, and dressing. Toss until rocket is completely coated with dressing.

3 Top with chèvre (if using) to serve.

Fresh figs are a seasonal delight. If you can't find any, you can use fresh peaches, apricots, pears, or even segmented blood oranges. Use whatever fresh fruit is in season for this versatile recipe.

EACH SERVING HAS:

Calories	Total Fat	Carbohydrate	Protein
435	33g	33g	9g

Ruby beetroots and crisp raw carrots are tossed in a sesame-packed dressing of tahini and zahtar.

Beetroot and Carrot Slaw
with Tahini and Zahtar

15 MINUTES TO 24 HOURS | **NONE** | **SERVES 2**

INGREDIENTS

2 medium beetroots, trimmed and peeled

3 medium carrots, trimmed

2 large beetroot leaves, woody stems removed

1 tbsp extra virgin olive oil

2 tsp lemon juice

1 garlic clove, finely chopped

1 tbsp tahini (sesame seed paste)

½ tsp zahtar

1 tbsp toasted sesame seeds (white or black)

METHOD

1 Using the grater disk on a food processor, shred beetroots and carrots. (Alternatively, use a hand grater to make medium shreds.) Using a sharp knife, thinly slice beetroot leaves.

2 In a small bowl, whisk olive oil, lemon juice, garlic, tahini, and zahtar until fully combined to make dressing. Alternatively, place ingredients into a small jam jar, cover tightly with a lid, and shake vigorously until fully combined.

3 In a large bowl, combine beetroots, carrots, beetroot leaves, and dressing. Toss until vegetables are fully coated with dressing. Top with sesame seeds.

4 Serve immediately, or leave to marinate for up to 24 hours in the fridge.

Variation: This salad is also excellent with 2 medium apples and 2 medium raw kohlrabi or jicama instead of beetroots and carrots to make **Apple and Kohlrabi Slaw with Tahini and Zahtar.**

Zahtar is a traditional Middle Eastern and North African spice blend made of dried thyme, oregano, marjoram, toasted sesame seeds, salt, and often sumac. It can be found in many specialist grocery shops and spice shops, and online.

EACH SERVING HAS:

| Calories 272 | Total Fat 14g | Carbohydrate 34g | Protein 6g |

paleo
pastas

How can pasta be Paleo? With vegetable noodles! These dishes make it easy to add a few extra servings to your diet using root vegetables, courgette, and even shaved asparagus. Simply use a vegetable spiralizer, julienne peeler, or julienne plate on a mandoline to create your noodles. Or, while a bit more time consuming, use a regular peeler to make flat vegetable ribbons to use like linguine. Raw or cooked, these pastas make vibrant vegetable-based meals.

Mellow **celery root** makes the perfect base for this pasta with **sweet fresh clams,** juicy cherry tomatoes, golden toasted garlic, and a spritz of **white wine.**

Celery Root Spaghetti
with Clams

 15 MINUTES   **12 MINUTES**   **SERVES 4**

INGREDIENTS

Juice of 1 medium lemon (about 2 tbsp)

2 large celery roots

2 tbsp extra virgin olive oil

2 garlic cloves, finely chopped

20 cherry tomatoes, halved

¼ tsp crushed red pepper flakes

2 tbsp dry white wine

1kg (2lb) small live hard-shell clams, shells rinsed

30g (1oz) flat-leaf parsley

¼ tsp sea salt

¼ tsp freshly ground black pepper

METHOD

1 Fill a large bowl, deep enough to hold both celery roots, halfway with water. Add 1 tablespoon lemon juice.

2 Working on 1 celery root at a time, trim both root and stem ends. Using a paring knife or vegetable peeler, carefully peel off rough outer skin. Immediately submerge peeled root in lemon water. Repeat with second celery root.

3 Use a vegetable spiralizer to create thin spaghetti strands with each celery root. Return "noodles" to lemon water. Alternatively, use a vegetable peeler to create thin ribbons or strips.

4 Place a large frying pan over medium-high heat. When the pan is hot, add olive oil and wait 30 seconds.

5 Add garlic, cherry tomatoes, and crushed red pepper flakes, and sauté, stirring constantly, for 2 to 3 minutes, or until garlic is golden brown and tomatoes have blistered.

6 Add dry white wine and continue to stir, scraping up any browned bits off the bottom of the frying pan. Add hard-shell clams, cover, and cook for 5 minutes.

7 Uncover, stir, and add strained celery root noodles. Cover again and cook for 3 to 4 minutes, or until clams have opened.

8 Remove from heat. Stir in flat-leaf parsley, sea salt, black pepper, and remaining tablespoon lemon juice. Discard any clams that didn't open, and serve immediately.

EACH SERVING HAS:

Calories **309**   Total Fat **9g**   Carbohydrate **27g**   Protein **18g**

Thinly shaved asparagus ribbons and **sweet peas** are served carbonara style: with **crisp pancetta nuggets** and a **decadently rich sauce.**

Shaved Asparagus
Carbonara

15 MINUTES **10 MINUTES** **SERVES 2**

INGREDIENTS

- 450g (1lb) thick asparagus spears (about 20 spears), trimmed
- 115g (¼ lb) thick sliced bacon or pancetta, diced
- 1 medium shallot, finely chopped
- 2 tbsp dry white wine
- 85g (3oz) shelled peas or thawed previously frozen peas
- 1 large egg yolk
- ¼ tsp freshly ground black pepper

METHOD

1 Using a mandoline or vegetable peeler, carefully slice asparagus spears lengthways into long ribbons. Set aside.

2 Place a large frying pan over medium-low heat. Add bacon and slowly brown, turning once or twice, until crisp (about 3 to 4 minutes). Remove from the pan and place on kitchen paper to absorb grease.

3 Reheat the frying pan with any remaining bacon grease over medium-low heat.

4 Add shallot and cook, stirring frequently, for 1 to 2 minutes, or until slightly translucent.

5 Carefully add dry white wine (watching out for any grease splatters), and stir with a wooden spoon to loosen any browned bits from the bottom of the pan.

6 Add peas and cook for 1 minute. Turn off heat and move the frying pan off the heat. Add asparagus, cover, and steam lightly for 1 minute.

7 Add egg yolk to hot vegetables, and toss to combine and cook egg. Top with crisp bacon and black pepper to serve.

Variation: If you don't have a good way to shave asparagus, this recipe is just as tasty with courgette or celery root noodles instead.

EACH SERVING HAS:

Calories **376**   Total Fat **19g**   Carbohydrate **16g**   Protein **14g**

A pesto of mild **carrot tops** and **toasted hazelnuts** steals the show, paired with spiralized carrots, sun-dried tomatoes, artichoke hearts, and **sautéed chicken**.

Carrot Spirals with
Carrot Top Pesto

15 MINUTES | **5 MINUTES** | **SERVES 4**

INGREDIENTS

680g (1½ lb) carrots, with greens

30g (1oz) basil, chopped

2 garlic cloves

Juice of ½ medium lemon (about 1 tbsp)

2 tbsp pumpkin seeds

30g (1oz) toasted hazelnuts

120ml (4fl oz), plus 1 tbsp extra virgin olive oil

½ tsp sea salt

225g (½lb) boneless, skinless chicken breast, diced

15g (½oz) sun-dried tomatoes, coarsely chopped

60g (2oz) canned artichoke hearts, chopped

METHOD

1 Trim greens off carrots. Cut off long stems and discard. Roughly chop leaves.

2 In a food processor, pulse carrot top leaves, basil, garlic, lemon juice, pumpkin seeds, toasted hazelnuts, 120ml (4fl oz) olive oil, and sea salt until a smooth paste forms. Set aside.

3 Use a vegetable spiralizer to create thin spaghetti strands with each carrot. Alternatively, use a vegetable peeler to create thin ribbons or strips.

4 Place a large frying pan over medium-high heat. When the skillet is hot, add remaining tablespoon olive oil and wait 30 seconds.

5 Add diced chicken breast and sauté, stirring frequently, for 2 to 3 minutes, or until chicken is browned and cooked through.

6 Add sun-dried tomatoes, artichoke hearts, and carrot spirals, and cook for 1 to 2 minutes, or until heated through. Remove from heat.

7 Add several tablespoons pesto to the frying pan and toss to fully coat. Serve immediately.

EACH SERVING HAS:

Calories **545**   Total Fat **38g**   Carbohydrate **35g**   Protein **20g**

Rich, **sweet potato spirals** are tossed in a **spicy tomato sauce** and topped with **hearty chicken meatballs** brimming with **fresh vegetables** and **oregano**.

Sweet Potato Pasta with
Tomatoes and Meatballs

20 MINUTES   **50 MINUTES**   **SERVES 4**

INGREDIENTS

- 2 medium sweet potatoes, peeled
- 2 tbsp extra virgin olive oil
- 1 medium carrot, peeled and finely chopped
- 4 cloves garlic, finely chopped
- 2 x 400g can chopped tomatoes
- 1 tbsp Italian seasoning
- ¼ tsp crushed red pepper flakes (optional)
- 1½ tsp sea salt
- ½ tsp freshly ground black pepper
- 1 red pepper, deseeded and coarsely chopped
- 4 medium white button mushrooms
- 20g (¾oz) oregano, chopped
- 450g (1 lb) ground chicken

METHOD

1 Use a vegetable spiralizer to create thin spaghetti strands with each sweet potato. Alternatively, use a vegetable peeler to create thin ribbons or strips. Set aside.

2 Place a medium casserole over medium heat. When the casserole is hot, add 1 tablespoon olive oil and wait 30 seconds.

3 Add carrot and sauté, stirring frequently, for 4 to 5 minutes, or until carrot pieces are slightly softened. Add 2 garlic cloves and continue to cook 1 to 2 minutes, or until garlic is golden brown.

4 Add tomatoes, Italian seasoning, crushed red pepper flakes (if using), ½ teaspoon sea salt, and black pepper, and stir to combine. Reduce heat to low, cover, and simmer, stirring occasionally, for 25 minutes.

5 Place red pepper, white button mushrooms, oregano, remaining

2 cloves garlic, and remaining teaspoon sea salt in a food processor. Pulse for 15 to 30 seconds, until vegetables are roughly chopped.

6 Combine vegetables with ground chicken. Form into 12 meatballs.

7 When sauce is ready, stir in sweet potato noodles, cover, and steam for 10 minutes, or until noodles are slightly tender. Remove from heat.

8 Place a medium frying pan over medium-high heat. When it's hot, add remaining tablespoon olive oil and wait 30 seconds.

9 Fry meatballs in oil, turning to brown on all sides, for 7 to 10 minutes, or until cooked through.

10 Top pasta and sauce with meatballs to serve.

EACH SERVING HAS:

Calories **377**   Total Fat **13g**   Carbohydrate **31g**   Protein **34g**

Tangy **piquillo peppers** and **spiced chorizo** are tossed with **fresh mussels** and served over al dente **fresh courgette noodles.**

Courgette Noodles with
Piquillo Peppers and Mussels

20 MINUTES   **12 MINUTES**   **SERVES 2**

INGREDIENTS

- 450g (1lb) live mussels, with beards removed
- 2 medium courgettes, trimmed
- ¼ tsp sea salt
- 2 tbsp extra virgin olive oil
- ½ medium yellow onion, diced
- 25g (1oz) hard Spanish chorizo, diced
- 3 piquillo peppers or 1 roasted red pepper, thinly sliced
- 120ml (4fl oz) dry white wine
- handful of coriander, chopped

METHOD

1 Soak live mussels in a bowl of cool water for 15 minutes. Rinse thoroughly.

2 Meanwhile, use a vegetable spiralizer to create thin spaghetti strands with each courgette. Alternatively, use a vegetable peeler to create thin ribbons or strips.

3 Place courgette noodles in a colander in the sink. Sprinkle with sea salt and gently massage with clean hands to make sure salt fully covers noodles.

4 After mussels have been rinsed, place a large frying pan over medium-high heat. When the pan is hot, add olive oil and wait 30 seconds.

5 Add onion and sauté, stirring frequently, for 3 to 5 minutes, or until onion is slightly translucent. Add Spanish chorizo and piquillo peppers, and cook, stirring occasionally, for 2 minutes.

6 Give courgette noodles a squeeze to get rid of any extra moisture, and place in the frying pan along with dry white wine and mussels.

7 Increase heat to high, cover, and cook for 4 to 5 minutes, or until mussels open.

8 Discard any unopened mussels. Stir, garnish with coriander, and serve immediately.

EACH SERVING HAS:

Calories **442** Total Fat **23g** Carbohydrate **25g** Protein **34g**

soups

Nothing beats a warm, satisfying bowl of soup on a cold day – unless it's a fresh, chilled bowl of gazpacho on a simmering summer afternoon! Whatever the weather calls for, this chapter provides an option. Cold, hot, broth-based, creamy purée, or hearty stew, these recipes are simple and delicious.

Luscious ripe cantaloupe – brightened with **fresh lemon,** a hint of **ginger root,** and just a **touch of basil** – makes this chilled soup a summertime treat.

Chilled Cantaloupe and
Blood Orange Soup

2 HOURS, 15 MINUTES — **NONE** — **SERVES 3**

INGREDIENTS

- 1 ripe cantaloupe (about 1.5kg/3lb)
- Juice of 1 medium blood orange (about 3 tbsp)
- 2 tsp freshly grated ginger root
- Juice of 1 lemon (about 2 tbsp)
- 2 tbsp extra virgin olive oil
- ½ tsp sea salt
- 1 tbsp mint, finely chopped

METHOD

1 Cut cantaloupe. Remove seeds and rind, and slice into 2.5cm (1-inch) cubes.

2 Place cantaloupe, orange juice, ginger root, lemon juice, olive oil, and sea salt in a blender.

3 Pulse for 1 to 2 minutes, or until puréed. Chill for at least 2 hours.

4 Ladle soup into bowls and garnish with fresh mint to serve.

Variation: Use honeydew melon and fresh basil instead of cantaloupe and mint, and top with chopped macadamia nuts, to make **Chilled Honeydew and Basil Soup.**

Fresh ginger root is a natural anti-inflammatory, digestive aid, and immune booster. The sweet melon in this recipe tones it down, but you may wish to add more if you love the unbridled flavour.

EACH SERVING HAS:

| Calories 187 | Total Fat 10g | Carbohydrate 25g | Protein 2g |

This classic Spanish soup has **mellow toasted garlic, smoked paprika,** and a **creamy poached egg.**

Sopa de Ajo

5 MINUTES | **20 MINUTES** | **SERVES 2**

INGREDIENTS

2 tbsp extra virgin olive oil

10 garlic cloves, finely chopped

2 tsp Spanish paprika

960ml (1 ¾ pints) chicken stock or broth

½ tsp sea salt

2 large eggs

1 tbsp coriander, chopped

METHOD

1 Heat a medium saucepan over medium heat. When the pan is hot, add olive oil and wait 30 seconds.

2 Add garlic and cook, stirring continuously, for about 60 seconds, or until garlic is golden brown.

3 Add Spanish paprika and stir for 15 seconds. Add chicken stock and sea salt. Stir once, and continue to cook until small bubbles come to the surface (about 10 minutes).

4 While soup is simmering, gently break each egg into a separate small bowl.

5 With soup still simmering, gently slide each egg into hot liquid, using a small spoon to ladle a bit of stock over each egg.

6 Cover the pan and cook until egg whites are solid, about 3 to 5 minutes.

7 Ladle soup into bowls and top with fresh coriander to serve.

Variation: Pair this soup with Cauliflower Steaks with Ras el Hanout for a heartier meal. Or slice a boneless, skinless chicken thigh and simmer it in broth for 10 to 12 minutes, until cooked through, for some extra protein.

EACH SERVING HAS:

Calories 236	Total Fat 19g	Carbohydrate 8g	Protein 9g

Light and fresh, this quintessential summer soup has **ripe tomatoes, cucumber, bell pepper, fresh lemon juice,** and a dash of **hot sauce.**

Gazpacho

15 MINUTES | **NONE** | **SERVES 4**

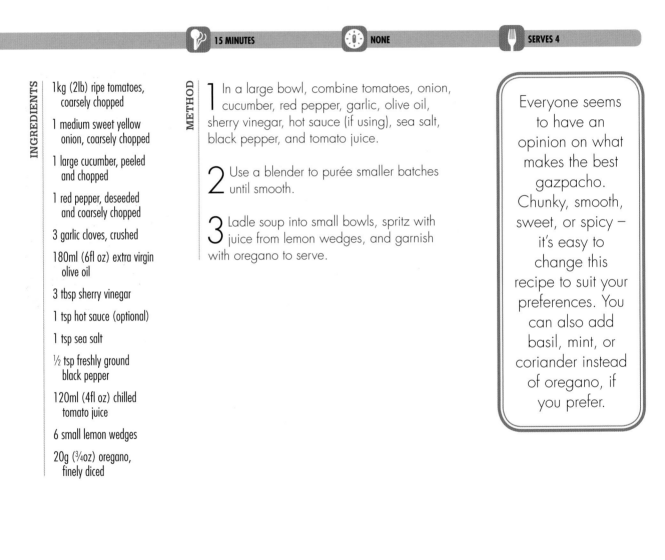

INGREDIENTS

1kg (2lb) ripe tomatoes, coarsely chopped

1 medium sweet yellow onion, coarsely chopped

1 large cucumber, peeled and chopped

1 red pepper, deseeded and coarsely chopped

3 garlic cloves, crushed

180ml (6fl oz) extra virgin olive oil

3 tbsp sherry vinegar

1 tsp hot sauce (optional)

1 tsp sea salt

½ tsp freshly ground black pepper

120ml (4fl oz) chilled tomato juice

6 small lemon wedges

20g (¾oz) oregano, finely diced

METHOD

1 In a large bowl, combine tomatoes, onion, cucumber, red pepper, garlic, olive oil, sherry vinegar, hot sauce (if using), sea salt, black pepper, and tomato juice.

2 Use a blender to purée smaller batches until smooth.

3 Ladle soup into small bowls, spritz with juice from lemon wedges, and garnish with oregano to serve.

Everyone seems to have an opinion on what makes the best gazpacho. Chunky, smooth, sweet, or spicy – it's easy to change this recipe to suit your preferences. You can also add basil, mint, or coriander instead of oregano, if you prefer.

EACH SERVING HAS:

| Calories 268 | Total Fat 20g | Carbohydrate 25g | Protein 4g |

Subtle celery root and creamy leeks classically flavour this simple soup, seasoned with white pepper and topped with a sprinkle of fresh chives.

Leek and Celeriac Soup

20 MINUTES   **30 MINUTES**   **SERVES 4**

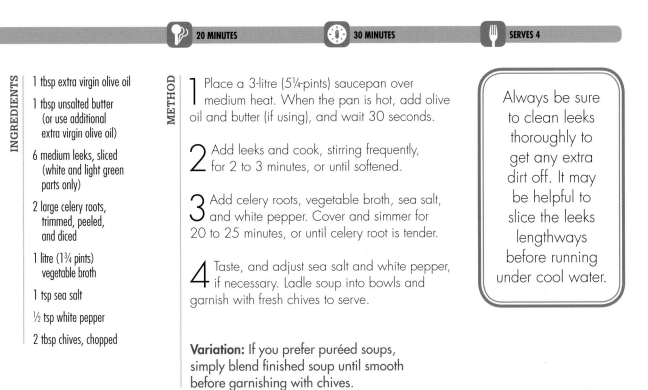

INGREDIENTS

- 1 tbsp extra virgin olive oil
- 1 tbsp unsalted butter (or use additional extra virgin olive oil)
- 6 medium leeks, sliced (white and light green parts only)
- 2 large celery roots, trimmed, peeled, and diced
- 1 litre (1¾ pints) vegetable broth
- 1 tsp sea salt
- ½ tsp white pepper
- 2 tbsp chives, chopped

METHOD

1 Place a 3-litre (5¼-pints) saucepan over medium heat. When the pan is hot, add olive oil and butter (if using), and wait 30 seconds.

2 Add leeks and cook, stirring frequently, for 2 to 3 minutes, or until softened.

3 Add celery roots, vegetable broth, sea salt, and white pepper. Cover and simmer for 20 to 25 minutes, or until celery root is tender.

4 Taste, and adjust sea salt and white pepper, if necessary. Ladle soup into bowls and garnish with fresh chives to serve.

Variation: If you prefer puréed soups, simply blend finished soup until smooth before garnishing with chives.

Always be sure to clean leeks thoroughly to get any extra dirt off. It may be helpful to slice the leeks lengthways before running under cool water.

EACH SERVING HAS:

Calories **237**   Total Fat **7g**   Carbohydrate **40g**   Protein **2g**

Subtle fennel and **saffron** flavour this French stew, allowing the soft and delicious tastes of the **fresh seafood** to shine through.

Bouillabase

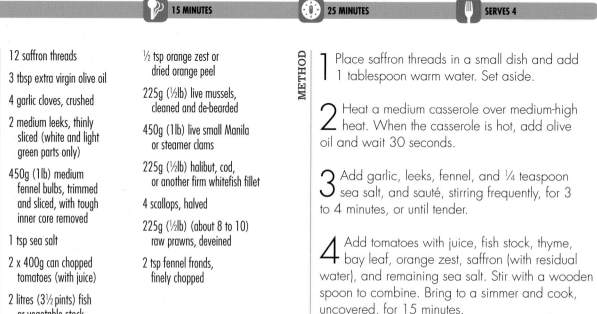

15 MINUTES   **25 MINUTES**   **SERVES 4**

INGREDIENTS

12 saffron threads

3 tbsp extra virgin olive oil

4 garlic cloves, crushed

2 medium leeks, thinly sliced (white and light green parts only)

450g (1lb) medium fennel bulbs, trimmed and sliced, with tough inner core removed

1 tsp sea salt

2 x 400g can chopped tomatoes (with juice)

2 litres (3½ pints) fish or vegetable stock

3 thyme sprigs

1 bay leaf

½ tsp orange zest or dried orange peel

225g (½lb) live mussels, cleaned and de-bearded

450g (1lb) live small Manila or steamer clams

225g (½lb) halibut, cod, or another firm whitefish fillet

4 scallops, halved

225g (½lb) (about 8 to 10) raw prawns, deveined

2 tsp fennel fronds, finely chopped

METHOD

1 Place saffron threads in a small dish and add 1 tablespoon warm water. Set aside.

2 Heat a medium casserole over medium-high heat. When the casserole is hot, add olive oil and wait 30 seconds.

3 Add garlic, leeks, fennel, and ¼ teaspoon sea salt, and sauté, stirring frequently, for 3 to 4 minutes, or until tender.

4 Add tomatoes with juice, fish stock, thyme, bay leaf, orange zest, saffron (with residual water), and remaining sea salt. Stir with a wooden spoon to combine. Bring to a simmer and cook, uncovered, for 15 minutes.

5 Add mussels and clams. Stir to make sure all shells are submerged. Cover and cook for 2 to 3 minutes, or until mussels and clams open.

6 Add halibut, scallops, and prawns, and stir. Cook for 30 seconds, or until opaque. Discard any mussels or clams that didn't open, as well as bay leaf.

7 Ladle soup into bowls, garnish with fennel fronds, and serve immediately.

EACH SERVING HAS:

Calories **411**
Total Fat **12g**
Carbohydrate **32g**
Protein **34g**

Straight from Tuscany, this savoury soup has a **rich broth** flavoured with **pancetta** and **aromatic vegetables,** and topped with **salty Parmigiano-Reggiano cheese.**

Soup alla Canavese

10 MINUTES   **45 MINUTES**   **SERVES 4**

INGREDIENTS

- 60g (2oz) pancetta or bacon, diced
- 1 tbsp unsalted butter (optional)
- 1 medium yellow onion, diced
- 2 garlic cloves, finely chopped
- 2 medium carrots, diced
- 1 large celery stalk, diced
- 3 tbsp tomato paste
- 1 tsp dried sage
- 1 tsp sea salt
- ½ tsp freshly ground black pepper
- 500g (1lb 2oz) cauliflower florets, cut into small pieces
- 6 leaves cavolo nero, woody stems removed
- 1 bay leaf
- 1¼ litres (2 pints) chicken stock
- 60g (2oz) Parmigiano-Reggiano cheese, grated (optional)

METHOD

1 Heat a large soup pot or casserole over medium-high heat. When the pot is hot, add pancetta. Cook, stirring frequently, for 2 to 3 minutes, or until pancetta is golden and crisp.

2 Add butter (if using), onion, and garlic. Sauté, stirring frequently, for 3 to 5 minutes, or until onion is translucent and garlic is aromatic.

3 Add carrots, celery, tomato paste, sage, sea salt, and black pepper. Stir, and cook for 2 minutes.

4 Add cauliflower, cavolo nero, bay leaf, and chicken stock, and stir. Reduce heat to medium-low, cover, and simmer for 30 to 35 minutes, or until vegetables are tender. Remove and discard bay leaf.

5 Ladle soup into bowls and top with grated Parmigiano-Reggiano cheese (if using) to serve.

EACH SERVING HAS:

| Calories 262 | Total Fat 12g | Carbohydrate 27g | Protein 13g |

vegetables

While vegetables star in so many recipes throughout this book, this chapter focuses on seasonal sides and mains. Often, with little more than good olive oil and a bit of sea salt, the naturally delicious flavours of fresh, seasonal produce shine.

Local farmer's markets are a valuable resource for sourcing exceptional vegetables, as you'll only be able to purchase what's currently in season. Soon you'll learn what time of year to expect certain vegetables and how to plan your menu accordingly.

Sweet roasted carrots are drizzled with **lemon juice, honey,** and **crisp cumin seeds** and served with a tangy side of **full-fat yogurt.**

Roasted Carrots with
Cumin and Yogurt

10 MINUTES   **30 MINUTES**   **SERVES 4**

INGREDIENTS

- 450g (1lb) small carrots, trimmed and halved lengthways
- 2 tbsp extra virgin olive oil
- 1 tsp raw honey
- ½ tsp sea salt
- ½ tsp freshly ground black pepper
- 1 tsp whole cumin seeds
- ½ medium lemon, cut into 4 wedges
- 80ml (2fl oz) full-fat yogurt or full-fat coconut cream (optional)

METHOD

1 Preheat the oven to 220°C (425°F).

2 In a medium bowl, toss carrots in olive oil and raw honey.

3 Spread carrots evenly over a metal baking sheet. Sprinkle with sea salt, black pepper, and cumin seeds.

4 Bake for 25 to 30 minutes, or until tender.

5 Squeeze fresh lemon juice over top and serve alongside yogurt for dipping.

This simple side is an absolute showstopper when you use purple, orange, yellow, and red carrots. These gorgeous rainbow carrots can often be found year-round at most high-end markets.

EACH SERVING HAS:

Calories	Total Fat	Carbohydrate	Protein
109	7g	11g	1g

Geometric Romanesco florets, paired with **pine nut crumbles**, are pan-seared until **golden brown** and served with **velvety saffron alioli**.

Romanesco with Pine Nuts and Saffron Alioli

Romanesco with Pine Nuts

10 MINUTES | **6 MINUTES** | **SERVES 4**

INGREDIENTS

2 tbsp extra virgin olive oil

680g (1½lb) Romanesco, cut into small florets

2 tbsp toasted pine nuts, finely chopped or ground

¼ tsp coarse sea salt

1 tbsp lemon juice

METHOD

1 Place a large cast-iron frying pan over medium-high heat. When the pan is hot, add olive oil and wait 30 seconds.

2 Add Romanesco and sauté, not stirring, for 2 to 3 minutes, or until deep golden brown on one side. Stir carefully and turn heat down to low.

3 Sprinkle toasted pine nuts, sea salt, and lemon juice on top. Cover and steam for 2 to 3 minutes, or until Romanesco is tender.

4 Let cool slightly before serving with Saffron Alioli.

Romanesco is a gorgeous brassica, closely related to both broccoli and cauliflower. It's quite distinct, due to the geometric pattern that looks like a fractal. While its texture is similar to cauliflower, the taste is slightly nuttier than its traditional counterpart.

EACH SERVING HAS:

| Calories | 150 | Total Fat | 10g | Carbohydrate | 14g | Protein | 1g |

Saffron Alioli

INGREDIENTS

6 to 8 saffron threads

1 tsp warm water

1 large garlic clove, pressed or very finely chopped

¼ tsp sea salt

¼ tsp Dijon mustard

1 large egg yolk, at room temperature

180ml (6fl oz) extra virgin olive oil, at room temperature

1 tbsp lemon juice

METHOD

1 Place saffron threads in 1 teaspoon warm water and leave to sit for 5 minutes.

2 Using the broad side of a knife, scrape garlic clove with sea salt until a fine paste forms. Alternatively, use a pestle and mortar or a press to mash garlic into a smooth paste with no remaining chunks.

3 Place garlic paste, mustard, saffron threads (with residual water), and egg yolk into a wide-mouth 378-ml (1-pint) jam jar. Using an immersion blender, pulse mixture for 15 seconds, or until fully blended.

4 Add 2 drops olive oil and blend for 10 seconds. Add 2 more drops olive oil and blend for 10 seconds.

5 Continue adding oil 1 teaspoon at a time and blending at 10-second intervals until a mayonnaise consistency begins to form. At that point, pour in remaining olive oil and blend until fully incorporated.

6 Add lemon juice and blend until combined. Taste and adjust salt or lemon as needed. Serve with Romanesco with Pine Nuts.

EACH SERVING HAS:

Calories	126	Total Fat	14g	Carbohydrate	0g	Protein	0g

Bright radicchio is roasted to mellow the bitterness, slathered in **North African chermoula,** and topped with **crunchy toasted walnuts.**

Roasted Radicchio with
Chermoula and Walnuts

| 15 MINUTES | 20 MINUTES | SERVES 6 |

INGREDIENTS

30g (1oz) coriander

handful of flat-leaf parsley

6 garlic cloves, sliced

1 tsp ground cumin

1 tsp smoked paprika

¾ tsp sea salt

¼ tsp cayenne pepper

120ml (4fl oz) extra
   virgin olive oil

2 tbsp lemon juice

3 heads radicchio, quartered

60g (2oz) walnuts, chopped

METHOD

1 Preheat the oven to 200°C (400°F).

2 To make chermoula, combine coriander, parsley, garlic, cumin, paprika, sea salt, cayenne pepper, olive oil, and lemon juice in a food processor. Pulse for 30 seconds, or until a paste forms. Taste and adjust seasonings, if desired.

3 Toss radicchio quarters in just enough chermoula to coat. Spread radicchio on a baking tray. Bake for 12 to 15 minutes, turning once, until wilted and tender.

4 Meanwhile, place walnuts in a small frying pan over low heat. Toast, stirring frequently, for 3 to 4 minutes, or until aromatic. Remove from the pan immediately.

5 To serve, top roasted radicchio with toasted walnuts.

Chermoula is traditionally used as a topping for fish or seafood, but is just as tasty on vegetables, chicken, or lamb.

EACH SERVING HAS:

Calories **247**   Total Fat **25g**   Carbohydrate **6g**   Protein **3g**

Crunchy Brussels sprouts and **mild flat-leaf parsley** are brightened with a squeeze of **fresh lemon juice** and topped with **toasty hazelnuts**.

Shaved Brussels sprouts
with Lemon and Parsley

10 MINUTES   **5 MINUTES**   **SERVES 4**

INGREDIENTS

1kg (2lb) fresh Brussels sprouts, trimmed

1 tbsp extra virgin olive oil

handful of flat-leaf parsley, chopped

Juice of 1 lemon (about 2 tbsp)

¼ tsp sea salt

¼ tsp freshly ground black pepper

60g (2oz) toasted hazelnuts, chopped

METHOD

1 Shred Brussels sprouts using a mandoline or the grater plate of a food processor, or by slicing thinly with a knife.

2 Place a large frying pan over medium heat. When the pan is hot, add olive oil and wait 30 seconds.

3 Add Brussels sprouts and sauté, stirring frequently, for 1 to 2 minutes, or until sprouts are vivid green but still crisp.

4 Stir in parsley, lemon juice, sea salt, and black pepper. Remove from heat.

5 Top with toasted hazelnuts to serve.

Variation: To make **Shaved Brussels Sprouts and Apple with Basil,** substitute fresh basil forflat-leaf parsley, and grate a fresh apple to add in to Brussels sprouts just before serving for a hint of sweetness.

This recipe proves that Brussels sprouts don't have to be fully cooked to be enjoyable. Raw Brussels sprouts are an excellent salad or slaw base, and add a bit of colour variety and a lot of fresh crunch to any vegetable mix.

EACH SERVING HAS:

| Calories 222 | Total Fat 13g | Carbohydrate 24g | Protein 10g |

Rich and robust Lebanese seven-spice blend seasons **earthy mushrooms** and **tomatoes,** which are baked inside vibrant purple aubergine.

Stuffed Aubergine with Lebanese Seven-Spice Blend

15 MINUTES   **1 HOUR**   **SERVES 4**

INGREDIENTS

- 2 medium aubergines, about 20cm (8in) long
- 2 tbsp, plus 1 tsp extra virgin olive oil
- 1 tsp sea salt
- ½ tsp freshly ground black pepper
- 1 medium yellow onion, diced
- 4 garlic cloves, finely chopped
- 450g (1lb) medium cremini mushrooms, diced
- 2 medium tomatoes, diced
- 1 tbsp Lebanese seven-spice blend
- handful of flat-leaf parsley, chopped
- handful of coriander, chopped
- 2 tbsp pine nuts, chopped

METHOD

1 Preheat the oven to 220°C (425°F).

2 Cut aubergines in half lengthways. Using a spoon, scoop out and discard seeds and flesh, leaving a 1.25cm (½-inch) rim of aubergine.

3 Brush inside of each half lightly with 1 teaspoon olive oil. Sprinkle with ½ teaspoon sea salt and black pepper.

4 Place halves face up in a shallow baking dish. Bake for 15 to 20 minutes, or until lightly golden brown.

5 Meanwhile, place a medium frying pan over medium-high heat. When it's hot, add 2 tablespoons olive oil and wait 30 seconds.

6 Add onion, garlic, and mushrooms, and sauté, stirring, for 4 to 6 minutes, or until onion is translucent and mushrooms are soft.

7 Reduce heat to medium-low. Add tomatoes, Lebanese seven-spice blend, and remaining sea salt, and cook for 5 minutes, stirring frequently. Remove from heat. Stir in parsley and coriander.

8 Remove golden aubergine halves from the oven. Reduce the oven temperature to 180°C (350°F).

9 Spoon vegetable mixture evenly into hollowed-out aubergine halves. Sprinkle with pine nuts.

10 Line the baking dish with foil and place aubergine halves on top. Bake for 15 to 20 minutes, or until halves are tender. Leave to cool slightly before serving.

EACH SERVING HAS:

| Calories 222 | Total Fat 12g | Carbohydrate 28g | Protein 5g |

These sometimes **spicy**, sometimes **mild**, **seasonal peppers** are **pan roasted** to perfection and tossed in nothing more than **good olive oil** and **coarse sea salt**.

Roasted Padróns
with Sea Salt

5 MINUTES | **10 MINUTES** | **SERVES 5**

INGREDIENTS

450g (1lb) whole Padrón peppers

1 tbsp high-quality extra virgin olive oil

½ tsp coarse sea salt

METHOD

1 Place a medium cast-iron frying pan over medium-high heat.

2 When the skillet is hot, place as many whole Padrón peppers on the bottom of the frying pan as will fit. Keep a large bowl nearby, as well as a pair of tongs.

3 Cook peppers for 4 to 6 minutes, or until skins begin to blister and brown. Carefully flip peppers as needed to cook all sides evenly. Transfer peppers to the bowl when uniformly browned and blistered. Repeat with any remaining peppers.

4 When all peppers have been cooked, add olive oil and sea salt, and toss to combine.

5 Serve whole peppers immediately with a small bowl on the side to collect discarded stems.

Make sure to keep the pepper stems intact. They make excellent handles for holding the warm peppers.

EACH SERVING HAS:

| Calories 94 | Total Fat 4g | Carbohydrate 2g | Protein 1g |

Roasted fennel, caramelized in **fresh orange juice**, is topped with **liquorice-like tarragon** and **pecans** coated with just the right amount of **sweet** and **spice**.

Fennel with Tarragon
and Spiced Pecans

Fennel with Tarragon

5 MINUTES · **20 MINUTES** · **SERVES 4**

INGREDIENTS

4 small fennel bulbs
(or 2 large bulbs)

1 tbsp extra virgin olive oil

¼ tsp sea salt

2 tsp tarragon, chopped

2 tbsp orange juice

METHOD

1 Trim fronds and thinner stalks off each fennel bulb. Also trim each stem end. Cut halves into .5cm (¼-inch) slices, removing tough inner core as you slice.

2 In a medium bowl, combine olive oil, sea salt, and tarragon. Add fennel and toss to coat completely.

3 Place a large cast-iron frying pan over medium heat. When the pan is hot, add fennel mixture and sauté, stirring frequently, for 15 to 20 minutes, or until golden brown and caramelized.

4 Add orange juice to the hot frying pan and stir, scraping any browned bits off the bottom of the skillet.

5 Serve warm and top with Spiced Pecans.

EACH SERVING HAS:

Calories **107**   Total Fat **4g**   Carbohydrate **18g**   Protein **3g**

Spiced Pecans

INGREDIENTS

- 2 tbsp coconut sugar
- ½ tsp sea salt
- ½ tsp cayenne pepper
- ¼ tsp allspice
- ½ tsp cinnamon
- 225g (8oz) raw pecan halves
- 1 egg white, slightly beaten

METHOD

1 Preheat the oven to 150°C (300°F).

2 Cut a piece of baking parchment to line the bottom of a large baking tray (or use a silicone sheet liner).

3 In a medium bowl, combine coconut sugar, sea salt, cayenne pepper, allspice, and cinnamon.

4 In a separate bowl, toss pecans in egg white to coat completely. Using a slotted spoon or fork, remove pecans and toss in seasoning mixture.

5 Spread coated pecans on the baking tray. Bake for about 20 minutes, stirring occasionally, until crisp. Serve by sprinkling on Fennel with Tarragon.

EACH SERVING HAS:

Calories 226	Total Fat 21g	Carbohydrate 8g	Protein 4g

Thick, meaty slices of **cauliflower** are **blackened** in a **rich 12-spice blend** with a punch of piquant **cayenne**.

Cauliflower Steaks with
Ras El Hanout

5 MINUTES   **6 MINUTES**   **SERVES 2**

INGREDIENTS

1 large head cauliflower

3 tsp extra virgin olive oil

2 tbsp ras el hanout

¼ tsp cayenne pepper

½ tsp sea salt

METHOD

1 Using a large chef's knife, carefully cut cauliflower head through stem into 3-cm (1¼-inch) slices. You may wish to cut it in half first, to make it easier to slice.

2 In a small bowl, combine 1 teaspoon olive oil, ras el hanout, cayenne pepper, and sea salt. Rub mixture on all sides of cauliflower steaks.

3 Place a large frying pan over medium-high heat. When the pan is hot, add remaining olive oil and wait 30 seconds.

4 Place cauliflower steaks in hot oil. Fry without moving for 2 to 3 minutes, or until dark golden brown. Turn steaks and cook for an additional 2 to 3 minutes on remaining side.

5 Serve warm alongside fresh or steamed greens, or another vegetable side.

Variation: To make **Paprika Cauliflower Steaks,** simply replace ras el hanout and cayenne pepper with 1 tablespoon smoked paprika, 1 teaspoon ground cumin, and 2 teaspoons granulated garlic.

EACH SERVING HAS:

Calories **171**   Total Fat **8g**   Carbohydrate **22g**   Protein **8g**

Toasty oven-roasted spring peas and **pearl onions** are tossed in **fresh mint** and a **splash of lemon,** and topped with paper-thin slices of **salty, dry-cured ham.**

Spring Peas and Pearl
Onions with Mint

| 5 MINUTES | 20 MINUTES | SERVES 4 |

INGREDIENTS

2 tbsp extra virgin olive oil

8 small pearl onions, quartered

325g (11oz) fresh spring peas, stems trimmed

¼ tsp sea salt

⅛ tsp freshly ground black pepper

10 mint leaves, chopped

1 tsp lemon juice

14g (½ oz) serrano ham or prosciutto, finely chopped (optional)

METHOD

1 Preheat the oven to 230°C (450°F).

2 Cut a piece of baking parchment to line the bottom of a large baking tray (or use a silicone sheet liner).

3 In a large bowl, toss olive oil, pearl onions, spring peas, sea salt, and black pepper until vegetables are fully coated. Spread vegetables out evenly on the sheet.

4 Bake for 8 minutes. Remove the sheet from the oven, stir with a wooden spoon, and return to the oven for 8 to 10 minutes, or until vegetables are tender.

5 Toss roasted vegetables with mint and lemon juice, and top with serrano ham (if using). Serve warm.

Variation: If you'd like to skip any extra nitrates that can be naturally found or added in cured pork products, feel free to substitute 30g (1oz) sliced and pitted black olives instead to still get that salty component.

EACH SERVING HAS:

| Calories **177** | Total Fat **7g** | Carbohydrate **21g** | Protein **8g** |

Lush green chard leaves and colourful stems are punched up with **browned garlic** and **fiery crushed red pepper flakes**.

Braised **Chard**

10 MINUTES   **5 MINUTES**   **SERVES 4**

INGREDIENTS

450g (1lb) Swiss chard

1 tbsp extra virgin olive oil

2 garlic cloves, thinly sliced

1 tsp crushed red pepper flakes

¼ tsp sea salt

METHOD

1 Using a knife, carefully separate Swiss chard stems from leaves. Coarsely chop leaves and finely slice stems.

2 Heat a large frying pan over medium-high heat. When the pan is hot, add olive oil and wait 30 seconds.

3 Add garlic and Swiss chard stems, and sauté, stirring frequently, for 30 seconds to 1 minute, or until garlic is very aromatic and beginning to turn golden brown.

4 Add Swiss chard leaves, crushed red pepper flakes, and sea salt. Continue to sauté, stirring frequently, for 1 minute, or until leaves wilt.

5 Remove from heat and serve immediately.

Variation: This recipe is fantastic with any type of seasonal dark, leafy green. Mustard greens, cavolo nero, beet greens, or carrot tops are all highly recommended substitutions for Swiss chard. You may need to cook certain tougher greens longer than tender Swiss chard leaves, however.

This recipe is so easy and versatile, you may find yourself using it as a side for grilled meat, the base of a unique salad, or a bed for an Olive Oil–Fried Egg.

EACH SERVING HAS:

| Calories 60 | Total Fat 4g | Carbohydrate 5g | Protein 2g |

seafood

Seafood can be a bit intimidating for a beginning cook. These recipes will have you cooking like a pro in no time, with instructions on everything from choosing and cleaning live shellfish to properly searing fish so it doesn't fall apart in the pan. With flavoursome fresh herbs, sauces, and marinades, it's easy to make seafood a fast and convenient part of your weekly meal plan.

Charred calamari is marinated in **garlic, lemon,** and **bright ground cumin,** with a spicy pop of **Calabrian chillies.**

Calamari with Cumin

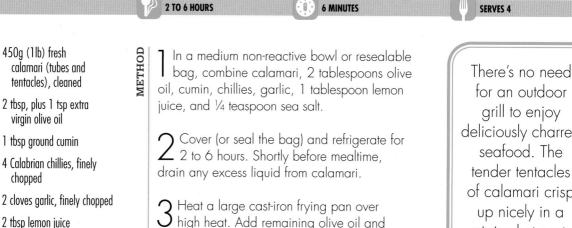

2 TO 6 HOURS   **6 MINUTES**   **SERVES 4**

INGREDIENTS

450g (1lb) fresh calamari (tubes and tentacles), cleaned

2 tbsp, plus 1 tsp extra virgin olive oil

1 tbsp ground cumin

4 Calabrian chillies, finely chopped

2 cloves garlic, finely chopped

2 tbsp lemon juice

½ tsp coarse sea salt

2 tbsp oregano leaves

METHOD

1 In a medium non-reactive bowl or resealable bag, combine calamari, 2 tablespoons olive oil, cumin, chillies, garlic, 1 tablespoon lemon juice, and ¼ teaspoon sea salt.

2 Cover (or seal the bag) and refrigerate for 2 to 6 hours. Shortly before mealtime, drain any excess liquid from calamari.

3 Heat a large cast-iron frying pan over high heat. Add remaining olive oil and wait 30 seconds.

4 Spread calamari evenly in the bottom of the hot pan and cook for 2 to 3 minutes, or until edges are charred. Turn calamari and cook for 2 to 3 minutes on the remaining side.

5 Remove calamari from the frying pan. Sprinkle with remaining lemon juice, remaining sea salt, and oregano leaves to serve.

There's no need for an outdoor grill to enjoy deliciously charred seafood. The tender tentacles of calamari crisp up nicely in a piping-hot cast-iron frying pan.

EACH SERVING HAS:

| Calories 192 | Total Fat 14g | Carbohydrate 3g | Protein 15g |

Flaky tuna steak is served alongside a crisp salad of **fresh orange slices,
crunchy raw fennel,** and **olives,** with a **whole-grain mustard vinaigrette.**

Tuna Steak with Orange and Fennel Salad

15 MINUTES | **6 MINUTES** | **SERVES 2**

INGREDIENTS

2 x 110g (4oz) tuna steaks

¼ tsp sea salt

½ tsp freshly ground
   black pepper

1 medium fennel bulb,
   trimmed and halved

4 tsp extra virgin olive oil

1 tsp lemon juice

1 tsp wholegrain mustard

1 tsp dill, chopped

1 medium orange, peeled
   and chopped

60g (2oz) kalamata olives

METHOD

1 Season both sides of tuna steaks lightly with sea salt and ¼ teaspoon black pepper.

2 Cut fennel into 5-mm (¼-inch) slices, removing tough inner core as you slice.

3 In a small bowl, whisk 2 teaspoons olive oil, lemon juice, mustard, dill, and remaining black pepper until fully combined to make dressing. Alternatively, place ingredients into a small jam jar, cover tightly with a lid, and shake vigorously until fully combined.

4 Place a medium frying pan over medium heat. When the pan is hot, add remaining olive oil and wait 30 seconds.

5 Place tuna steaks in hot oil. Cook for 1 to 3 minutes per side, until surfaces are golden brown and centre is cooked as desired.

6 Meanwhile, combine fennel, orange, olives, and dressing in a medium bowl. Toss until coated.

7 Serve tuna steaks over orange and fennel salad.

EACH SERVING HAS:

| Calories 320 | Total Fat 12g | Carbohydrate 26g | Protein 29g |

Baked whole sea bass is stuffed with **gremolata:** a bright combination of zingy lemon zest, ample amounts of **garlic,** and **fresh parsley.**

Baked Sea Bass with Gremolata

15 MINUTES · **25 MINUTES** · **SERVES 2**

INGREDIENTS

Zest of 2 medium lemons (about 4 tsp)

5 garlic cloves, finely chopped

handful of flat-leaf parsley, finely chopped

2 tsp capers, rinsed

¾ tsp sea salt

1 whole sea bass, about 450g (1lb), cleaned

1 tbsp extra virgin olive oil

¼ tsp freshly ground black pepper

METHOD

1 Preheat the oven to 250°C (475°F).

2 To make gremolata, in a small bowl, combine lemon zest, garlic, parsley, capers, and ¼ teaspoon sea salt.

3 Stuff cavity of sea bass with gremolata. Place stuffed sea bass on a parchment-lined baking sheet.

4 Drizzle sea bass with olive oil and sprinkle with remaining sea salt and black pepper.

5 Bake for 20 to 25 minutes, or until eyes have turned opaque white and flesh just under the skin flakes easily with a fork.

6 Remove branzino skin, head, and bones before serving.

Variation: To make **Baked Sea Bass with Fennel,** simply fill branzino cavity with ½ medium fennel bulb, ½ lemon, and 2 garlic cloves, all thinly sliced, instead of gremolata.

EACH SERVING HAS:

| Calories 306 | Total Fat 12g | Carbohydrate 5g | Protein 44g |

Delicate sole fillets are paired with a salad of **sweet heirloom tomatoes,** buttery Castelvetrano olives, and a pop of **toasted pine nuts.**

Sole with Fresh Tomato Salad

15 MINUTES   **5 MINUTES**   **SERVES 2**

INGREDIENTS

- 2 x 110g (4oz) sole fillets
- ½ tsp sea salt
- ¼ tsp freshly ground black pepper
- 2 tbsp extra virgin olive oil
- 225g (½lb) heirloom tomatoes, diced
- 60g (2oz) Castelvetrano olives
- 2 tbsp basil, chopped
- 1 tbsp lemon juice
- 2 tbsp toasted pine nuts

METHOD

1 Season both sides of sole fillets lightly with ¼ teaspoon sea salt and black pepper.

2 Place a medium frying pan over medium-high heat. When the pan is hot, add 1 tablespoon olive oil and wait 30 seconds.

3 Place fillets in hot oil. Cook for 1 to 2 minutes per side, until surfaces are golden brown and centres flake easily with a fork.

4 Meanwhile, in a large bowl, combine tomatoes, olives, basil, lemon juice, toasted pine nuts, remaining sea salt, and remaining olive oil. Toss to coat.

5 Serve sole fillets over fresh tomato salad.

This recipe is best in the height of summer, when heirloom tomatoes have fully ripened in the sun and are bursting with natural sweetness and flavour. For other times of the year, try using sweet cherry or grape tomatoes as a substitute.

EACH SERVING HAS:

Calories **345**   Total Fat **25g**   Carbohydrate **16g**   Protein **20g**

Succulent prawns flavoured with **garlic** are gently sautéed and served with a warmly spiced salad of **grated carrot** and **sweet dried currants**.

Garlic Ginger Prawns with
Spiced Carrot-Currant Salad

Garlic Ginger Prawns

35 MINUTES   **5 MINUTES**   **SERVES 4**

INGREDIENTS

60ml (2fl oz) extra virgin olive oil

4 garlic cloves, finely chopped

2 tsp fresh ginger root, grated

16 large prawns

sea salt

METHOD

1 In a medium bowl, combine olive oil, garlic, and ginger. Add prawns and toss to coat. Cover the bowl and refrigerate for at least 30 minutes.

2 Shortly before mealtime, place a large frying pan over medium-high heat.

3 When the frying pan is hot, add prawns with remaining garlic and ginger–infused oil. Sauté, stirring frequently, for 2 to 4 minutes, or until prawns are bright pink.

4 Remove from heat, season with sea salt to taste, and serve immediately with Spiced Carrot-Currant Salad.

EACH SERVING HAS:

Calories 265   Total Fat 19g   Carbohydrate 1g   Protein 19g

Spiced Carrot-Currant Salad

15 MINUTES   NONE   SERVES 4

INGREDIENTS

- 4 tsp extra virgin olive oil
- 60ml (2fl oz) orange juice
- 2 tsp ras el hanout
- ¼ tsp sea salt
- 680g (1½lb) carrots, grated
- 60g (2oz) dried currants
- handful of coriander, chopped
- 60g (2oz) pistachios

METHOD

1 In a small bowl, whisk olive oil, orange juice, ras el hanout, and sea salt until fully combined to make dressing. Alternatively, place ingredients in a small jam jar, cover tightly with a lid, and shake vigorously until fully combined.

2 In a salad bowl, combine carrots, currants, coriander, pistachios, and dressing. Toss to coat completely.

3 Serve over Garlic Ginger Prawns.

EACH SERVING HAS:

Calories	262	Total Fat	12g	Carbohydrate	36g	Protein	6g

Tender white fish, simmered in fragrant spices and hearty vegetables, is topped with crunchy toasted almonds and fresh coriander.

White Fish Tagine with Tomatoes

15 MINUTES   **40 MINUTES**   **SERVES 4**

INGREDIENTS

- 1 large aubergine, cut into 2.5cm (1in) cubes
- 3 tbsp extra virgin olive oil (plus more for rubbing fish)
- 450g (1lb) skinless, boneless white fish fillets
- 1 tsp sea salt
- 1 small shallot, finely chopped
- 2 garlic cloves, sliced
- 1 tsp ground cinnamon
- 1 tsp ground cumin
- 1 tsp ground ginger
- ½ tsp turmeric
- ¼ tsp freshly ground black pepper
- 420g can chopped tomatoes, with juice
- 1 medium courgette, diced
- 1 medium carrot, peeled and diced
- 125g (4½oz) small cauliflower florets
- 2 tbsp capers
- 2 tbsp coriander, chopped
- 2 tbsp slivered almonds, lightly toasted

METHOD

1 Rub aubergine cubes with a bit of olive oil to keep from browning. Set aside. Sprinkle white fish fillets with ½ teaspoon sea salt. Place in the fridge for later use.

2 Heat a large casserole over medium-high heat. When it's hot, add olive oil and wait 30 seconds.

3 Add shallot and garlic, and sauté, stirring frequently, for 2 to 3 minutes, or until shallot is slightly translucent and garlic is golden brown.

4 Add cinnamon, cumin, ginger, turmeric, and black pepper. Stir, and cook for 30 seconds. Reduce heat to low.

5 Add tomatoes (with juice), aubergine, courgette, carrot, cauliflower, and remaining sea salt. Stir, cover, and simmer for 30 minutes.

6 Taste and adjust sea salt, if needed. Add capers and white fish fillets. Cover and simmer for 2 to 3 minutes, or until fish flakes with a fork.

7 Garnish with fresh cilantro and slivered almonds to serve.

EACH SERVING HAS:

Calories 280
Total Fat 12g
Carbohydrate 19g
Protein 5g

Sweet roasted peppers with **salty anchovies** and **buttery Castelvetrano olives** make the perfect light lunch paired with **grain-free bread** or crackers.

Roasted Peppers with
Anchovies and Castelvetranos

5 MINUTES **20 MINUTES** **SERVES 4**

INGREDIENTS

6 roasted red peppers, sliced

60g (2 oz) oil-packed anchovies, drained

2 garlic cloves, finely chopped

60g (2oz) pitted Castelvetrano olives, coarsely chopped

3 tbsp flat-leaf parsley, finely chopped

1 tbsp extra virgin olive oil

¼ tsp freshly ground black pepper

2 tsp lemon juice

METHOD

1 Preheat the oven to 220°C (425°F).

2 Place red peppers, anchovies, garlic, olives, parsley, olive oil, and black pepper in a shallow baking dish.

3 Bake, uncovered, for 15 to 20 minutes, or until anchovies crisp slightly on top.

4 Sprinkle with lemon juice and serve with Grain-Free Flatbread, Olive and Onion Focaccia, Nut and Seed Crackers.

To roast your own red peppers, simply cut each pepper in half, place skin-side up on a metal baking sheet, and grill on high until skins are charred and black. Transfer peppers immediately to a large resealable plastic bag, close the bag, and let steam for 15 minutes. Once steamed, peel skins from peppers, and cut away stems and white membranes.

EACH SERVING HAS:

Calories 192

Total Fat 14g

Carbohydrate 7g

Protein 5g

Hearty fillets of **salmon,** spiced with **zahtar,** are baked on a bed of **sweet butternut squash couscous** and drizzled with a **tangy tahini yogurt sauce.**

Salmon with Butternut Squash Couscous

15 MINUTES   30 MINUTES   SERVES 2

INGREDIENTS

- 1 small butternut squash (about 1kg/2 lb)
- 4 tsp extra virgin olive oil
- ¾ tsp sea salt
- 2 garlic cloves, finely chopped
- 1 tbsp preserved lemon peel, thinly sliced
- 2 tbsp flat-leaf parsley, chopped
- ½ medium red onion, thinly sliced
- 2 x 170g (6oz) boneless salmon fillets, about 3.75cm (1½in) thick
- 1 tbsp zahtar
- 2 tbsp tahini
- 60ml (2fl oz) full-fat yogurt or coconut yogurt
- 1 tbsp lemon juice
- 1 tbsp water

METHOD

1 Preheat the oven to 190°C (375°F).

2 Trim stem and blossom end off butternut squash and cut in half lengthways. Using a sturdy spoon, scoop out seeds and discard. Cut each half into half again to make quarters.

3 Using a sharp knife, carefully trim off butternut squash peel on each quarter. Cut each peeled quarter into thirds and place in a food processor. Pulse for 30 to 45 seconds, or until a coarse couscous consistency forms.

4 Transfer squash to a medium roasting pan or Dutch oven, along with 2 teaspoons olive oil, ½ teaspoon sea salt, garlic, preserved lemon peel, parsley, and red onion. Mix with a wooden spoon and spread out in the bottom of the pan.

5 Sprinkle salmon fillets with zahtar, remaining olive oil, and remaining ¼ teaspoon sea salt. Place fillets side by side, on top of vegetables, in the pan.

6 Bake, uncovered, for 25 to 30 minutes, or until vegetables are tender and salmon flakes easily with a fork.

7 Meanwhile, in a small bowl, combine tahini, full-fat yogurt, lemon juice, and water. Drizzle over cooked salmon and vegetables to serve.

Variation: This recipe can also be made with grated sweet potatoes or yams instead of butternut squash.

EACH SERVING HAS:

Calories 643	Total Fat 24g	Carbohydrate 72g	Protein 49g

Fresh mussels are lightly steamed in **garlic** and **white wine** and served alongside **crisp celeriac fries**.

Garlic Mussels and
Celeriac Fries

Garlic Mussels

5 MINUTES | **8 MINUTES** | **SERVES 4**

INGREDIENTS

1 tbsp extra virgin olive oil

4 garlic cloves, finely chopped

32 live mussels (about 1kg/2 lb), cleaned and de-bearded

120ml (4fl oz) dry white wine

½ tsp sea salt

1 tbsp lemon juice

15g (½oz) flat-leaf parsley, chopped

METHOD

1 Place a large frying pan over medium-high heat. When the pan is hot, add olive oil and wait 30 seconds.

2 Add garlic and sauté, stirring constantly, for 1 to 2 minutes, or until golden brown.

3 Add mussels and dry white wine. Cover immediately and simmer for 4 to 5 minutes, or until mussels open.

4 Discard any unopened mussels. Add sea salt, lemon juice, and parsley, and toss gently to combine. Serve immediately with Celeriac Fries.

EACH SERVING HAS:

| Calories | 281 | Total Fat | 16g | Carbohydrate | 8g | Protein | 11g |

Celeriac Fries

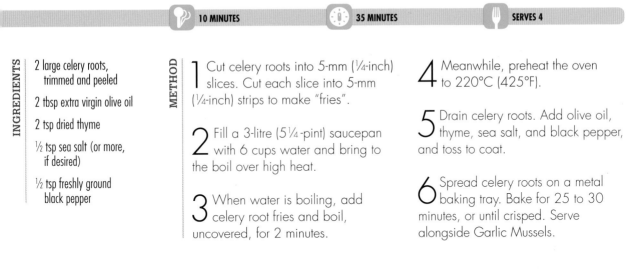

10 MINUTES | **35 MINUTES** | **SERVES 4**

INGREDIENTS

2 large celery roots, trimmed and peeled

2 tbsp extra virgin olive oil

2 tsp dried thyme

½ tsp sea salt (or more, if desired)

½ tsp freshly ground black pepper

METHOD

1 Cut celery roots into 5-mm (¼-inch) slices. Cut each slice into 5-mm (¼-inch) strips to make "fries".

2 Fill a 3-litre (5¼-pint) saucepan with 6 cups water and bring to the boil over high heat.

3 When water is boiling, add celery root fries and boil, uncovered, for 2 minutes.

4 Meanwhile, preheat the oven to 220°C (425°F).

5 Drain celery roots. Add olive oil, thyme, sea salt, and black pepper, and toss to coat.

6 Spread celery roots on a metal baking tray. Bake for 25 to 30 minutes, or until crisped. Serve alongside Garlic Mussels.

EACH SERVING HAS:

| Calories | 148 | Total Fat | 7g | Carbohydrate | 18g | Protein | 0g |

poultry

Poultry will never be dull again with this variety of recipes using chicken, turkey, duck, and poussin. With the right spices, marinades, and rubs, this lean protein will explode with flavour. This chapter teaches you techniques for preparing boneless, skinless cuts, as well as more flavoursome bone-in, skin-on choices.

Chicken thighs are rubbed with a **robust blend of paprika, cardamom, garlic,** and **ginger,** and roasted on top of **tender broccolini.**

Paprika-Rubbed Chicken with Broccolini

10 MINUTES   **45 MINUTES**   **SERVES 4**

INGREDIENTS

- 1 tsp smoked paprika
- 1 tsp cardamom
- ½ tsp granulated garlic
- ½ tsp ground ginger
- ¾ tsp sea salt
- ½ tsp freshly ground black pepper
- 4 large chicken thighs (680g/1½ lb), bone in and skin on
- 340g (¾ lb) broccolini, trimmed
- 3 tsp extra virgin olive oil
- 30g (1oz) toasted hazelnuts, chopped

METHOD

1 Preheat the oven to 190°C (375°F).

2 In a small bowl, combine smoked paprika, cardamom, garlic, ginger, ½ teaspoon sea salt, and black pepper.

3 Using clean hands, rub all sides of each chicken thigh with spice mixture. Be sure also to carefully reach under skin and rub flesh underneath with spices.

4 In a large mixing bowl, toss broccolini in 1 teaspoon olive oil and sea salt.

5 Heat a large ovenproof frying pan or casserole over medium-high heat. When the pan is hot, add remaining olive oil and wait 30 seconds, or until the pan begins to smoke lightly. Reduce heat to medium.

6 Place chicken thighs in the frying pan, skin-side down. Brown for 2 to 3 minutes per side, or until dark golden brown. Remove from the pan.

7 Place broccolini in the bottom of the hot frying pan. Add chicken thighs on top, skin-side up. Place the pan in the oven and bake for 25 to 35 minutes, or until chicken reaches an internal temperature of 75°C (165°F).

8 Top with toasted hazelnuts to serve.

EACH SERVING HAS:

Calories **479**   Total Fat **35g**   Carbohydrate **9g**   Protein **31g**

Spicy harissa-glazed wings are sweetened with a **hint of honey** and brightened with **fresh orange zest.**

Orange and Harissa-Glazed
Chicken Wings

1 HOUR, 15 MINUTES   **50 MINUTES**   **SERVES 4**

INGREDIENTS

8 whole chicken wings

1 tbsp extra virgin olive oil

½ tsp sea salt

2 tbsp raw honey

1½ tsp orange zest

1 tsp harissa

½ tsp granulated garlic powder

1 tbsp coriander, chopped

METHOD

1 To separate whole chicken wings, first identify drumettes (small leg bones), two-bone middle sections (called *flats*), and tiny wing tips.

2 Find joint between drumettes and flats. Using a sharp knife, cut directly through joint separation. Do the same between flats and wing tips. Repeat for all wings, and discard wing tips (or save for stock).

3 Rinse drumettes and flats with water to remove any bone fragments. Pat dry with kitchen paper.

4 Line a metal baking tray with foil. Place a metal cooling rack on top, and spread chicken pieces evenly on the rack. Place in the fridge, uncovered, for 60 minutes to dry chicken skin fully.

5 After chicken is dry, preheat the oven to 200°C (400°F).

6 Remove wings from the rack and, in a medium bowl, toss in olive oil and sea salt. Place on the rack again, and bake for 35 to 45 minutes, or until skin is golden and crisped.

7 Meanwhile, to make glaze, combine raw honey, orange zest, harissa, and garlic powder in a small bowl.

8 When chicken is done, brush with glaze and bake for 4 to 5 minutes, or until glaze is shiny and caramelized. Garnish with coriander to serve.

EACH SERVING HAS:

Calories 266	Total Fat 17g	Carbohydrate 9g	Protein 18g

Succulent seasoned duck breast is served on a vibrant salad of radicchio, pomegranate, oranges, and **fresh mint,** with an **orange juice-Dijon vinaigrette.**

Spiced Duck with Raddichio and Pomegranate

15 MINUTES　　**8 MINUTES**　　**SERVES 2**

INGREDIENTS

6 tsp extra virgin olive oil

1 tbsp orange juice

2 tsp shallot, finely chopped

1 tsp Dijon mustard

1 tsp raw honey

½ tsp sea salt

¼ tsp freshly ground
　black pepper

1 small boneless duck breast
　(about 225g/8 oz), skin on

½ tsp ras el hanout

1 medium head radicchio,
　coarsely chopped

1 small orange, peeled
　and segmented

60g (2oz) pomegranate seeds

handful of mint leaves

60g (2oz) pecans, chopped

METHOD

1 In a small bowl, whisk 5 teaspoons olive oil, orange juice, shallot, mustard, raw honey, ¼ teaspoon sea salt, and black pepper until fully combined to make dressing. Alternatively, place ingredients into a small jam jar, cover tightly with a lid, and shake vigorously until fully combined.

2 Sprinkle skin side of duck breast with remaining sea salt and ras el hanout.

3 Place a small frying pan over medium-high heat. When the pan is hot, add remaining olive oil and wait 30 seconds.

4 Place duck breast skin-side down in the pan. Immediately lower temperature to medium-low. Cook duck for 2 to 3 minutes, or until skin is a deep golden brown and crisp. Turn duck breast and finish cooking to desired temperature, about 3 to 5 minutes.

5 Meanwhile, in a medium bowl, combine radicchio, orange segments, pomegranate seeds, mint, pecans, and dressing. Toss to coat.

6 When duck is cooked through, cut breast into 6 slices. Divide salad into bowls and top with duck breast slices to serve.

EACH SERVING HAS:

Calories **561**　　Total Fat **37g**　　Carbohydrate **30g**　　Protein **32g**

Crisped chicken thighs are simmered on top of **cauliflower rice** and **sofrito:** an aromatic blend of **sautéed onions, garlic, red pepper,** and **tomato.**

Chicken Sofrito with
Cauliflower Rice

 20 MINUTES　　**45 MINUTES**　　**SERVES 6**

INGREDIENTS

2 tsp sea salt

2 tsp sweet paprika

6 chicken thighs, bone in and skin on

1 tbsp extra virgin olive oil

1 medium yellow onion, diced

4 garlic cloves, sliced

1 jalapeño, deseeded and finely chopped

1 medium red pepper, deseeded and diced

1 tbsp thyme leaves

¼ tsp cayenne pepper (optional)

1 large tomato, diced

240ml (8fl oz) chicken stock or broth

1 medium head cauliflower, riced

Juice of 1 medium lemon (about 2 tbsp)

60g (2oz) slivered almonds, toasted

METHOD

1 Preheat the oven to 190°C (375°F). In a small bowl, mix sea salt and sweet paprika. Spread mixture on skin side of each chicken thigh.

2 Place a large cast-iron frying pan or casserole over medium-high heat. When the pan is hot, add olive oil and wait 30 seconds.

3 Place chicken thighs, seasoned-side down, in hot oil. Cook for 2 to 3 minutes, or until skins are nicely browned. Turn and repeat on other side. Remove chicken from the pan and set aside.

4 Add yellow onion to the hot skillet and sauté, stirring frequently, for 3 minutes. Add garlic and continue to sauté for 1 minute, or until onion is slightly translucent and garlic is fragrant and golden.

5 Add jalapeño, red pepper, thyme, cayenne pepper (if using), and tomato, and cook for another 5 to 6 minutes, or until most of liquid in the bottom of the pan cooks off.

6 Add chicken stock, riced cauliflower, lemon juice, and slivered almonds, and stir to combine. Place chicken thighs, skin-side up, on top of cauliflower mixture.

7 Bake, uncovered, for 20 to 25 minutes, or until chicken is cooked through. Serve.

EACH SERVING HAS:

Calories **374**　　　Total Fat **23g**　　　Carbohydrate **13g**　　　Protein **30g**

Juicy roast chicken is baked with **garlic, lemon,** and **sage,** and served alongside a **hearty root vegetable assortment.**

Whole Roast Chicken
with Root Vegetables

40 MINUTES   **1 HOUR, 30 MINUTES**   **SERVES 6**

INGREDIENTS

1 chicken (about 2.25kg/5lb)

4 tbsp extra virgin olive oil

1½ tsp sea salt

1 tsp freshly ground black pepper

10 sage leaves, finely chopped

10 garlic cloves, crushed

1 lemon, quartered

1 large sweet yellow onion, halved and sliced

2 large sweet potatoes or yams, diced

1 large celery root, peeled and diced

1 medium swede, peeled and diced

2 medium carrots, peeled and diced

METHOD

1 Preheat the oven to 220°C (425°F).

2 Remove any giblets or plastic wrappings from cavity of chicken. Rinse cavity (trying not to get too much water on skin), and pat dry with kitchen paper. Set chicken, breast-side up, in a large roasting pan.

3 Rub 2 tablespoons olive oil all over outside of chicken and between skin and flesh. Sprinkle chicken with 1 teaspoon sea salt and ½ teaspoon black pepper.

4 Stuff chicken cavity with sage, garlic, and lemon, and leave to rest on the kitchen counter for 20 minutes. Place the pan in the oven and bake for 30 minutes.

5 Meanwhile, in a large mixing bowl, place onion, sweet potatoes, celery root, swede, carrots, remaining olive oil, remaining sea salt, and black pepper. Stir until vegetables are fully coated.

6 After 30 minutes, remove chicken from the oven. Transfer root vegetables to the roasting pan (you may need to lift chicken out and place it on top of vegetables). Leave all oil in the pan, and make sure vegetables don't cover chicken.

7 Return chicken and vegetables to the oven, and bake for 45 to 60 minutes, or until chicken reaches an internal temperature of 75°C (165°F).

8 Remove from the oven, and let chicken rest for 15 minutes before slicing and serving with vegetables.

EACH SERVING HAS:

Calories **678**   Total Fat **33g**   Carbohydrate **15g**   Protein **78g**

Juicy grilled chicken breasts are marinated in **fresh citrus, ginger,** and **garlic,** and served on a bed of **peppery rocket.**

Citrus-Grilled Chicken
with Greens

4 TO 8 HOURS, 15 MINUTES   **20 MINUTES**   **SERVES 2**

INGREDIENTS

120ml (4fl oz) orange juice

2 tbsp lemon juice

2 tbsp lime juice

1 tbsp extra virgin olive oil

1 tsp freshly grated
ginger root

2 garlic cloves, finely chopped

450g (1lb) boneless,
skinless chicken breasts

¾ tsp sea salt

¼ tsp freshly ground
black pepper

115g (4oz) baby rocket or
mixed greens

60g (2oz) nuts of choice,
toasted and chopped

METHOD

1 In a medium glass or plastic container (or a large, sealable plastic bag), combine orange juice, lemon juice, lime juice, olive oil, ginger root, and garlic.

2 Place chicken breasts in the container, cover, and shake to fully coat. Refrigerate for 4 to 8 hours.

3 Shortly before mealtime, remove chicken from the fridge. Drain chicken from liquid (don't discard liquid) and place on a plate.

4 Preheat the grill to medium-high.

5 Meanwhile, in a small saucepan over medium-high heat, place reserved marinade. Bring to the boil for 5 minutes. Remove from heat to cool, and season with ¼ teaspoon sea salt (or more, if desired).

6 Sprinkle both sides of chicken breasts with remaining ½ teaspoon sea salt and black pepper.

7 When the grill is hot, place seasoned chicken on the grill. Cook, turning once, for 10 to 15 minutes, or until chicken reaches an internal temperature of 75°C (165°F).

8 To serve, slice chicken into thin strips. Divide baby rocket into 4 serving bowls and add chicken to each. Drizzle each bowl with boiled marinade as a dressing or sauce. Sprinkle with toasted nuts.

EACH SERVING HAS:

Calories **490**   Total Fat **32g**   Carbohydrate **12g**   Protein **43g**

Lean turkey kebabs – spiced up with **garlic, coriander,** and **cumin** – are served alongside **bright vegetable kebabs** and a **tahini yogurt sauce.**

Turkey Kebabs with
Courgette and Tahini

15 TO 45 MINUTES   **6 MINUTES**   **SERVES 4**

INGREDIENTS

2 medium courgettes trimmed and cut into 1.25cm (½in) slices

24 cherry tomatoes

¾ tsp sea salt

4 tsp extra virgin olive oil

1 tsp granulated garlic

1 tsp ground coriander

½ tsp ground cumin

2 spring onions, thinly sliced (white and light green parts only)

1 large egg, beaten

450g (1lb) ground turkey

2 tbsp tahini

60ml (2fl oz) full-fat yogurt or coconut yogurt

2 tsp lemon juice

1 tbsp water

2 tbsp oregano, chopped

METHOD

1 In a medium bowl, toss courgettes and cherry tomatoes with ¼ teaspoon sea salt and 2 teaspoons olive oil. Set aside.

2 In a second medium bowl, combine remaining sea salt, remaining olive oil, garlic, coriander, cumin, and spring onions, stirring with a wooden spoon.

3 Add egg and ground turkey, and stir with the wooden spoon until combined.

4 Divide turkey into 8 small balls. Form each ball around a skewer to create 10cm- (4-inch-) long kebabs. If using wooden skewers, soak skewers in water for at least 30 minutes beforehand. Set aside and wash hands with soap and water.

5 Thread remaining skewers with 3 tomatoes and 3 courgette slices, alternately. (Make sure to keep raw turkey skewers and vegetable skewers on separate surfaces.)

6 Preheat the grill to medium-high. While waiting for the grill to heat, in a small bowl, whisk tahini, full-fat yogurt, lemon juice, and water. Add oregano and stir. Set aside.

7 When the grill is hot, cook kebabs about 3 minutes on each side, or until cooked through. Serve 2 vegetable and 2 turkey kebabs per person with a side of tahini yogurt.

Variation: If you don't have a grill at home, you can place skewers on a grill pan and bake at 190°C (375°F) for 10 minutes. Turn kebabs and continue to cook for 10 to 15 minutes, or until cooked through.

EACH SERVING HAS:

Calories **318**   Total Fat **19g**   Carbohydrate **11g**   Protein **28g**

Warmly spiced **chicken thighs** are seared golden brown; simmered alongside plump **apricots**, **green olives**, and **almonds**; and served over **cauliflower florets**.

Chicken Tagine with
Apricots and Green Olives

15 MINUTES   **1 HOUR**   **SERVES 3**

INGREDIENTS

½ tsp ground cardamom

½ tsp ground ginger

½ tsp ground cinnamon

½ tsp turmeric

¾ tsp sea salt

¼ tsp freshly ground
   black pepper

225g (½lb) boneless,
   skinless chicken
   thighs, diced

2 tbsp extra virgin olive oil

60g (2oz) blanched almonds,
   coarsely chopped

4 garlic cloves, sliced

120ml (4fl oz) chicken stock

60g (2oz) dried apricots, chopped

60g (2oz) green olives, pitted

1 tbsp preserved lemon
   rind, thinly sliced

1 medium head cauliflower,
   cut into florets

handful of coriander, chopped

METHOD

1 In a medium bowl, combine cardamom, ginger, cinnamon, turmeric, sea salt, and black pepper.

2 Place chicken thighs in the bowl and rub spice mixture on all sides. Save any extra spice mixture.

3 Heat a large casserole over medium-high heat. When the casserole is hot, add olive oil and wait 30 seconds.

4 Add diced chicken and cook for about 2 to 3 minutes, or until browned. Turn meat to brown all sides. Remove chicken from the casserole and set aside.

5 Add almonds, garlic, and any residual spices to hot oil in the casserole, and sauté, stirring constantly, for 30 seconds, or until lightly fragrant.

6 Add chicken stock to the hot casserole and stir with a wooden spoon, scraping up any browned bits off the bottom.

7 Add apricots, green olives, and preserved lemon rind, and stir. Add cauliflower florets and gently stir again.

8 Place browned chicken on top. Cover and simmer for 45 to 50 minutes, or until chicken is cooked through.

9 Garnish warm chicken tagine with coriander to serve.

EACH SERVING HAS:

Calories **529**   Total Fat **33g**   Carbohydrate **37g**   Protein **30g**

Crisp roast chicken breasts are served with **garlic mashed sweet potatoes** and smothered in a **creamy leek sauce** with **fragrant thyme.**

Roast Chicken with
Creamy Leeks

10 MINUTES   **1 HOUR**   **SERVES 4**

INGREDIENTS

2 medium sweet potatoes, peeled and quartered

4 to 6 whole garlic cloves, peeled

360ml (12fl oz) chicken stock or broth

2 large chicken breasts, split, bone in and skin on

¾ tsp sea salt

½ tsp freshly ground black pepper

1 tbsp unsalted butter or ghee (or olive oil)

3 medium leeks, cleaned, trimmed, and sliced (white and light green parts only)

1 tsp thyme

1 tsp Dijon mustard

120ml (4fl oz) dry white wine

METHOD

1 Preheat the oven to 200°C (400°F).

2 Place sweet potatoes, garlic, and 240ml (8fl oz) chicken stock in a small ovenproof baking dish or casserole pan.

3 Place chicken breast halves, skin-side up, on top of sweet potatoes. Sprinkle breasts with ½ teaspoon sea salt and ¼ teaspoon black pepper.

4 Bake chicken, uncovered, for 45 to 60 minutes, or until it reaches an internal temperature of 75°C (165°F).

5 About 15 minutes before chicken is done, place a medium frying pan over medium-high heat.

6 When the pan is hot, add butter, leeks, remaining sea salt (if desired), remaining black pepper, and thyme. Sauté, stirring frequently, for 4 to 6 minutes, or until leeks are soft.

7 Add mustard, dry white wine, and remaining chicken stock. Cover and simmer until chicken is finished cooking.

8 When chicken is cooked, set aside to rest for 5 minutes. Transfer sweet potatoes, garlic, and remaining pan juices to a food processor, and purée until mashed.

9 Cut each chicken breast into slices. Serve with creamy leeks on top of mashed sweet potatoes.

EACH SERVING HAS:

| Calories 409 | Total Fat 13g | Carbohydrate 28g | Protein 39g |

beef, pork, and lamb

This chapter provides a few great recipes for beef, pork, and lamb – meats that are a part of the Mediterranean Paleo diet, but aren't encouraged daily. From simple Beef Kofta to extravagant Pork Loin Roulade, these recipes showcase these flavoursome meats.

If you can find an alternative grass-fed or pasture-raised option – such as elk, bison, or venison – you can always substitute these similar cuts into the recipes.

Tender roast beef and **vegetables** are slow cooked with **whole coriander** and served with a **vibrant tapenade of olive, nuts,** and **sherry vinegar.**

Coriander-Crusted Beef
with Olive-Nut Tapenade

Coriander-Crusted Beef

1 HOUR | **4 HOURS, 10 MINUTES** | **SERVES 10**

INGREDIENTS

2.25kg (5-lb) beef chuck or shoulder roast

60g (2oz) whole coriander seeds, crushed

1 tbsp sea salt

1 tsp freshly ground black pepper

3 tbsp extra virgin olive oil

1 large yellow onion, diced

5 garlic cloves, crushed

240ml (8fl oz) beef stock or broth, or water

5 medium carrots, trimmed and cut into 2.5cm (1-in) slices

1 celery root, peeled and diced into 2.5cm (1-in) cubes

METHOD

1 Season beef chuck roast on all sides with coriander, sea salt, and black pepper. Let roast sit at room temperature for 30 minutes.

2 Preheat the oven to 140°C (275°F).

3 Heat a large casserole or heavy-bottomed pan over high heat. When the casserole is hot, add 2 tablespoons olive oil and wait 30 seconds.

4 Place roast in hot oil for 2 to 3 minutes, or until a deep golden crust forms. Turn roast and repeat to brown all sides. Remove roast from the casserole.

5 Add remaining olive oil to the hot casserole. Add onion and garlic, and sauté, stirring frequently, for 2 to 3 minutes, or until onion is slightly translucent.

6 Add beef stock and stir with a wooden spoon to remove any browned bits from the bottom of the casserole. Remove from heat.

7 Add carrots and celery root, and place browned roast on top of vegetables. Cover and bake for 4 hours, or until beef is tender. Serve with Olive-Nut Tapenade.

EACH SERVING HAS:

| Calories | 422 | Total Fat | 22g | Carbohydrate | 10g | Protein | 46g |

Olive-Nut Tapenade

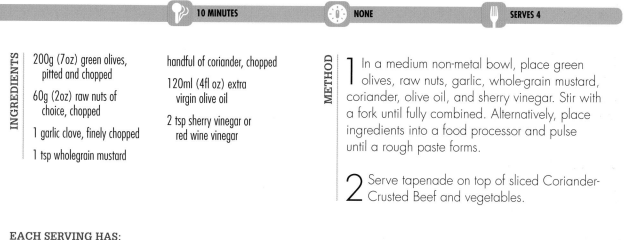

10 MINUTES　**NONE**　**SERVES 4**

INGREDIENTS

200g (7oz) green olives, pitted and chopped

60g (2oz) raw nuts of choice, chopped

1 garlic clove, finely chopped

1 tsp wholegrain mustard

handful of coriander, chopped

120ml (4fl oz) extra virgin olive oil

2 tsp sherry vinegar or red wine vinegar

METHOD

1 In a medium non-metal bowl, place green olives, raw nuts, garlic, whole-grain mustard, coriander, olive oil, and sherry vinegar. Stir with a fork until fully combined. Alternatively, place ingredients into a food processor and pulse until a rough paste forms.

2 Serve tapenade on top of sliced Coriander-Crusted Beef and vegetables.

EACH SERVING HAS:

| Calories | 140 | Total Fat | 14g | Carbohydrate | 4g | Protein | 1g |

Warmly spiced beef kebabs with **crunchy pine nuts** and **tart sumac** –
the perfect protein to serve alongside **fresh greens** or **steamed vegetables**.

Beef Kofta with Pine Nuts and Sumac

10 MINUTES — **6 MINUTES** — **SERVES 4**

INGREDIENTS

450g (1lb) lean ground beef

½ medium yellow onion, finely diced or grated

60g (2oz) toasted pine nuts, coarsely chopped

2 tbsp flat-leaf parsley, finely chopped

1 tsp ground cumin

1 tsp sumac

½ tsp ground cinnamon

¼ tsp cayenne pepper

1 tsp sea salt

¼ tsp freshly ground black pepper

METHOD

1 In a large bowl, thoroughly mix ground beef, onion, toasted pine nuts, parsley, cumin, sumac, cinnamon, cayenne pepper, sea salt, and black pepper.

2 Shape into 8 small balls. Mould 1 ball around each skewer (if using wooden skewers, soak in water for at least 30 minutes beforehand).

3 Preheat the grill to medium-high. When the grill is hot, cook kofta for about 3 minutes on each side, or until cooked through.

4 Serve warm with tzatziki, hummus, tapenade, zhug, tahini, or flatbread; eat them on their own as a snack; or have them as a breakfast or salad protein.

Variation: If you don't have a grill at home, you can still easily make these skewers as small "meatballs" instead. Skip the skewers and sauté in a bit of extra-virgin olive oil over medium-high heat for 3 to 5 minutes on each side, or until cooked through.

Kofta refers to any kebab made with ground meat in place of diced meat. Instead of marinating the meat to get extra flavour, the spices are mixed in. Feel free to use any kind of unseasoned ground meat in this recipe. Lamb, bison, and dark-meat chicken are excellent choices.

EACH SERVING HAS:

| Calories | 216 | Total Fat | 12g | Carbohydrate | 3g | Protein | 26g |

This extra-fancy dish – with **pounded pork loin** rolled in **figs, almonds, and fresh sage** – is great for holidays and special occasions.

Pork Loin Roulade with Figs and Almonds

25 MINUTES   **2 HOURS**   **SERVES 6**

INGREDIENTS

1.5kg (3lb) boneless pork loin

1½ tsp sea salt

1 tsp freshly ground black pepper

2 tbsp extra virgin olive oil

115g (4oz) yellow onion, diced

a handful of sage leaves, chopped

15g (¼ oz) slivered almonds, coarsely chopped

75g (2½ oz) dried figs, stems removed and coarsely chopped

1 tsp sherry vinegar

2kg (4lb) butternut squash, trimmed, deseeded, and sliced

300ml (10fl oz) vegetable or chicken stock

METHOD

1 Preheat the oven to 180°C (350°F).

2 Place pork loin on a chopping board. Using a sharp knife, butterfly loin by slicing parallel to the chopping board from right to left. Stop just short of the opposite edge, so flap stays attached by a 5-mm (¼-inch) section.

3 Open sliced loin flat, and place between two sheets of cling film on a sturdy surface. Using a meat tenderizer, pound loin to 1.25 to 2cm (½- to ¾-inch) thickness. Remove the cling film and sprinkle pork with sea salt and black pepper.

4 Place a medium frying pan over medium-high heat. When the pan is hot, add olive oil and wait 30 seconds.

5 Add onion and sauté, stirring frequently, for 3 to 5 minutes, or until onion is translucent.

6 Add sage, almonds, figs, and sherry vinegar, and cook, stirring occasionally, for 3 to 4 minutes, or until figs soften. Using a wooden spoon, spread mixture on loin.

7 Starting on one end, roll loin into a roulade. Using non-dyed cooking string, firmly tie centre of roulade together. Moving out to edge, tie pieces of string every 2.5cm (1 inch).

8 Place squash and vegetable stock in a casserole. Place roulade on top of squash.

9 Cover and bake, basting every 30 minutes, for 1 hour 15 minutes, or until pork reaches an internal temperature of 45°C (115°F). Remove the lid and bake for 30 minutes, or until pork reaches an internal temperature of 65°C (145°F).

10 Remove the string. Slice roulade and serve over squash.

EACH SERVING HAS:

| Calories 521 | Total Fat 25g | Carbohydrate 22g | Protein 51g |

Spicy Spanish **chorizo** is simmered in **apple cider** with **fresh peppers** and **sweet yellow onions**.

Chorizo in Sidra (Cider)

10 MINUTES   **55 MINUTES**   **SERVES 4**

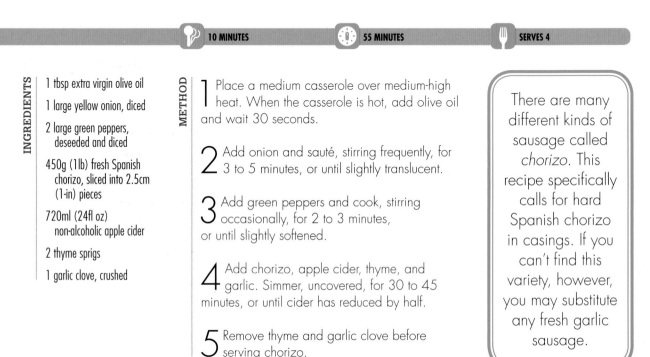

INGREDIENTS

1 tbsp extra virgin olive oil

1 large yellow onion, diced

2 large green peppers, deseeded and diced

450g (1lb) fresh Spanish chorizo, sliced into 2.5cm (1-in) pieces

720ml (24fl oz) non-alcoholic apple cider

2 thyme sprigs

1 garlic clove, crushed

METHOD

1 Place a medium casserole over medium-high heat. When the casserole is hot, add olive oil and wait 30 seconds.

2 Add onion and sauté, stirring frequently, for 3 to 5 minutes, or until slightly translucent.

3 Add green peppers and cook, stirring occasionally, for 2 to 3 minutes, or until slightly softened.

4 Add chorizo, apple cider, thyme, and garlic. Simmer, uncovered, for 30 to 45 minutes, or until cider has reduced by half.

5 Remove thyme and garlic clove before serving chorizo.

There are many different kinds of sausage called *chorizo*. This recipe specifically calls for hard Spanish chorizo in casings. If you can't find this variety, however, you may substitute any fresh garlic sausage.

EACH SERVING HAS:

| Calories 512 | Total Fat 34g | Carbohydrate 23g | Protein 29g |

Succulent lamb chops are smothered in a **sweet pomegranate, honey, and rosemary-infused glaze.**

Lamb Chops with
Pomegranate Glaze

40 MINUTES   30 MINUTES   SERVES 4

INGREDIENTS

- 8 small bone-in lamb chops
- 1 tsp sea salt
- ½ tsp freshly ground black pepper
- 240ml (8fl oz) pure pomegranate juice
- 2 tbsp raw honey
- 2 tbsp orange juice
- 2 tsp cognac or balsamic vinegar (optional)
- 1 sprig rosemary
- 1 tbsp extra virgin olive oil

METHOD

1 Season lamb chops on both sides with sea salt and black pepper. Leave out at room temperature for 30 minutes.

2 In a small saucepan, stir together pomegranate juice, raw honey, orange juice, and cognac (if using), and place over medium heat. Place rosemary sprig in the pan.

3 Bring to a simmer, stirring occasionally, for 18 to 20 minutes, or until reduced to a syrup-like consistency (glaze will continue to thicken as it cools). Remove from heat and discard rosemary sprig.

4 Heat a large frying pan over medium-high heat. When the pan is hot, add olive oil and wait 30 seconds.

5 Place seasoned lamb chops in the hot pan and cook for 3 to 4 minutes per side, or until cooked to desired temperature.

6 Brush with pomegranate glaze to serve.

EACH SERVING HAS:

| Calories 436 | Total Fat 8g | Carbohydrate 31g | Protein 30g |

This traditional Moroccan **sweet-and-savoury stew** features **warmly spiced lamb** simmered until tender, with **almonds, prunes, apricots,** and **cauliflower.**

Lamb and Prune Tagine

20 MINUTES | **1 HOUR, 10 MINUTES** | **SERVES 4**

INGREDIENTS

2 tbsp extra virgin olive oil

1kg (2lb) lamb shoulder

60g (2oz) blanched slivered almonds

1 medium onion, diced

3 garlic cloves, sliced

1 tsp sea salt

1 tsp ground ginger

1 tsp ground coriander

1 tsp turmeric

480ml (16fl oz) hot water

2 cinnamon sticks

1 large head cauliflower, cut into florets

45g (1½oz) prunes, pitted and quartered

60g (2oz) dried apricots, sliced

4 whole cloves

1 tbsp honey

1 tbsp orange blossom water (optional)

¼ tsp freshly ground nutmeg

handful of coriander, chopped

METHOD

1 Heat a large casserole over medium-high heat. When the casserole is hot, add olive oil and wait 30 seconds.

2 Add lamb shoulder and sear, stirring frequently, for 3 to 4 minutes, or until browned on all sides. Remove from the casserole and set aside.

3 Add almonds to hot oil in the casserole and sauté, stirring constantly, for 30 seconds, or until lightly golden. Add onion, garlic, and sea salt, and continue to cook, stirring frequently, for 1 to 2 minutes, or until slightly translucent.

4 Add ginger, coriander, and turmeric, and sauté for 30 seconds, or until highly fragrant.

5 Add browned lamb, hot water, and cinnamon sticks. Stir, cover, and simmer for 45 minutes.

6 Meanwhile, place cauliflower florets into a food processor. Pulse for 15 seconds, or until a rice-like consistency is achieved.

7 After 45 minutes, add prunes, apricots, cloves, honey, orange blossom water (if using), nutmeg, and cauliflower rice to the casserole. Cover and cook for an additional 20 minutes, or until lamb is tender. Garnish with coriander to serve.

EACH SERVING HAS:

Calories 676

Total Fat 34g

Carbohydrate 41g

Protein 57g

desserts

While dessert should not be the primary focus of the Mediterranean table, there is certainly a place for an indulgence. These recipes use low amounts of natural sugar or naturally sweet ingredients to satisfy that sweet craving once in a while. There is really no reason to feel guilty about dessert, so always remember to use whole ingredients for the most satisfying sweets.

Crackling coconut sugar is caramelized to dark amber on **glistening** orange, grapefruit, and **lemon slices.**

Citrus Brûlée

5 MINUTES　　　**8 MINUTES**　　　**SERVES 6**

INGREDIENTS

1 medium orange

1 medium pink grapefruit

1 lemon or lime

½ tsp ground ginger

50g (¾ oz) coconut sugar

METHOD

1 Arrange the oven rack to the highest position. Preheat the grill to high.

2 Slice orange, pink grapefruit, and lemon into 1.25cm (½-inch) slices, discarding end pieces of peel and any seeds.

3 Line a baking tray with foil. Spread citrus slices evenly on the foil-lined baking tray.

4 Sprinkle each slice with a small pinch of ginger. Next, sprinkle 1 to 2 teaspoons coconut sugar on each slice.

5 Place the baking tray on the highest oven rack and grill for 6 to 8 minutes, or until sugar caramelizes and turns a dark amber colour. Remove from the oven immediately. Be sure to watch constantly during the last few minutes. It takes only a few seconds to go from amber to burnt.

6 Cool citrus slices before serving. Don't eat rinds.

Variation: To make **Orange Blossom Brûlée,** use orange slices sprinkled with a touch of orange blossom water instead of ginger. Sprinkle with coconut sugar and grill as described.

Use any citrus you can find for this simple dessert. Try Meyer lemons, Key limes, tangelos, mandarins, or blood oranges. Just remember that lemons and limes are so tart they need extra coconut sugar; for variety, you can also pair them with sweeter citrus.

EACH SERVING HAS:

Calories 72

Total Fat 0g

Carbohydrate 19g

Protein 1g

Rich dark chocolate coated in **crumbly hazelnuts** surrounds **luscious fresh figs** for a decadent treat.

Chocolate-Covered Figs with Hazelnuts

1 TO 2 HOURS   **15 MINUTES**   **SERVES 6**

INGREDIENTS

12 figs

225g (8oz) dark or bittersweet chocolate chips (at least 60 percent cocoa)

60g (2oz) toasted hazelnuts, chopped

METHOD

1 Cut a square or rectangle of baking parchment to line the bottom of a small metal baking sheet or cake pan.

2 Carefully rinse figs, and pat dry with kitchen paper.

3 Place a small heavy-bottomed saucepan or double steamer over medium-low heat. A steamer is best, or you can make one with a metal bowl that fits over a saucepan with about 5cm (2 inches) of space between the bottom of the bowl and the bottom of the pan. Make sure to add 2.5cm (1 inch) of water to the bottom pan before heating.

4 Add dark chocolate chips to the saucepan and stir for 10 to 15 minutes, or until completely melted. Remove from heat.

5 Make sure figs are completely dry. Holding each fig by the stem, dip into melted chocolate, and sprinkle with chopped hazelnuts. Place on the baking parchment.

6 Place the baking sheet with figs in the fridge for 1 to 2 hours, or until chocolate hardens. Serve chilled.

Variation: In place of figs, use fresh ripe strawberries, cherries, or whatever fruit is sweet and in season to make this recipe year-round. Or use soft-pitted prunes or dried apricots for a winter variety.

EACH SERVING HAS:

Calories	Total Fat	Carbohydrate	Protein
336	21g	41g	5g

This **delicate almond cake** is simple and delicious. Flavoured with **almond extract** and **raw honey,** it's sure to please even the pickiest Paleo eaters.

Olive-Oil **Almond Cake**

10 MINUTES   **50 MINUTES**   **SERVES 10**

INGREDIENTS

- 250g (9oz) almond flour
- 85g (3oz) tapioca flour
- ¼ tsp sea salt
- ½ tsp baking soda
- 120ml (4fl oz) extra virgin olive oil
- 250ml (9fl oz) raw honey
- 4 large eggs
- 120ml (4fl oz) coconut milk or double cream
- 1½ tsp almond extract
- 1 tsp lemon juice
- 30g (1oz) sliced almonds, toasted

METHOD

1 Preheat the oven to 180°C (350°F).

2 In a large bowl, stir together almond flour, tapioca flour, sea salt, and baking soda with a fork until fully blended.

3 In a medium bowl, whisk together olive oil, 180ml (6fl oz) raw honey, eggs, coconut milk, and almond extract until fully blended. Add lemon juice and whisk again.

4 Pour liquid batter into dry mixture and stir with a wooden spoon until fully incorporated.

5 Lightly grease a silicone Bundt pan with olive oil. Alternatively, use a 23-cm (9-inch) round cake pan; however, a Bundt pan works best. If using a silicone pan, place on a sturdy metal baking sheet. If using a round cake pan, line the greased pan with a 23-cm (9-inch) circle of baking parchment.

6 Pour batter into the pan and leave to sit for 5 minutes.

7 Place the pan (on the baking sheet, if silicone) in the oven and bake for 40 to 50 minutes, or until a skewer inserted into cake comes out clean.

8 Leave to cool completely. Invert the pan over a serving plate and gently remove the pan from cake.

9 Drizzle with remaining raw honey and sprinkle with toasted almonds to serve.

EACH SERVING HAS:

Calories **386**   Total Fat **27g**   Carbohydrate **73g**   Protein **8g**

Ripe pears are simmered in **sticky-sweet Pedro Ximénez sherry** with **fragrant vanilla** and **cloves**.

Pears Poached in Sherry

5 MINUTES   **30 MINUTES**   **SERVES 4**

INGREDIENTS

2 medium firm pears

½ vanilla bean

480ml (16fl oz) Pedro Ximénez sherry

2 whole cloves

METHOD

1 Using a small paring knife or vegetable peeler, peel pears. Slice each pear in half lengthways. Using a melon baller or a sturdy metal spoon, remove core and seeds from each half.

2 Cut vanilla bean in half lengthways. Using the back of the knife (the blunt side), scrape out seeds. Reserve seeds and discard pods.

3 In a small saucepan over medium-high heat, pour Pedro Ximénez sherry. Add vanilla bean seeds and cloves, and stir.

4 When sherry begins to simmer, add pear halves and cook, turning occasionally, for 8 to 12 minutes, or until pears are tender, but not mushy.

5 Using a slotted spoon, remove pear halves from liquid and place each in a serving bowl to cool.

6 Remove sherry mixture from heat, and discard cloves. Drizzle a few spoonfuls of sherry mixture over each pear to serve.

Pedro Ximénez sherry, also known as PX sherry, is a sweet fermented wine made from late-harvested or sun-dried grapes, making the final product high in natural sugars. Use this sticky-sweet sherry for special occasions, or in limited quantities, as it's very high in carbohydrates.

EACH SERVING HAS:

Calories **140**   Total Fat **0g**   Carbohydrate **21g**   Protein **1g**

This **simple Sicilian iced dessert,** with **fresh strawberries** and **cooling mint tea,** is a refreshing summertime treat.

Strawberry-Mint Granita

4 HOURS, 45 MINUTES   **NONE**   **SERVES 5**

INGREDIENTS

- 300g (10oz) strawberries, sliced and with stalks removed
- 240ml (8fl oz) steeped mint tea, cooled
- 2 tbsp raw honey

METHOD

1 In a blender, combine strawberries, mint tea, and raw honey. Pulse to form a purée.

2 Spread mixture evenly in an 20-cm (8-inch) square baking dish. Place in the freezer for 30 minutes.

3 Stir mixture thoroughly with a metal fork, and spread evenly in the dish again. Repeat every 30 minutes for 3 to 4 hours.

4 Stir again before serving. Granita will hold for up to 12 hours.

Variation: To make **Cantaloupe-Mint Granita,** simply replace strawberries with 350g (12oz) chopped cantaloupe. Substitute any fresh, ripe fruit for an endless variety of granita flavours.

Making home-made mint tea is easy with fresh mint. Simply pour cup just-boiled water over 8 to 10 fresh mint leaves. Leave to steep for 10 to 15 minutes, and then remove mint leaves.

EACH SERVING HAS:

Calories **45**   Total Fat **0g**   Carbohydrate **11g**   Protein **0g**

Soft, sweet, and delicious, these **honey-caramelized peaches** are covered in **crunchy pistachios** and scented with **fragrant orange blossom water**.

Roasted Peaches with
Nuts and Honey

10 MINUTES   20 MINUTES   SERVES 6

INGREDIENTS

- 3 ripe peaches, pitted and halved
- 1 tsp extra virgin olive oil
- 2 tsp raw honey
- 2 tbsp pistachios coarsely chopped
- ½ tsp orange blossom water (optional)
- ⅛ tsp sea salt (optional)

METHOD

1 Preheat the oven to 200°C (400°F). Adjust the oven racks to the highest setting that will still allow for the baking tray.

2 Slice each peach half into 4 slices. Place peaches on a metal baking tray and drizzle with olive oil.

3 Bake for 10 minutes. Gently stir peaches with a wooden spoon, and bake for 5 minutes, or until softened.

4 Remove peaches from the oven, and turn the grill on high. Drizzle peaches with raw honey and sprinkle with pistachios.

5 Grill peaches for 1 to 3 minutes, or until deeply browned and caramelized on top. Watch carefully so peaches don't burn.

6 Right before serving, sprinkle with orange blossom water (if using) and sea salt (if using).

Variation: To make **Roasted Apricots with Pecans**, substitute 6 fresh apricots, quartered, instead of peaches, and use 2 tablespoons chopped pecans instead of pistachios.

EACH SERVING HAS:

Calories 53	Total Fat **1g**	Carbohydrate **11g**	Protein **1g**

Intensely dark chocolate cake, dense and chewy, is sprinkled with a dusting of smoked paprika.

Dark Chocolate
Paprika Cake

15 MINUTES   **1 HOUR, 5 MINUTES**   **SERVES 16**

INGREDIENTS

- 225g (8oz) unsalted butter, cut up
- 60ml (2fl oz) double cream
- 225g (8oz) bittersweet chocolate (at least 60 per cent cocoa), chopped
- 5 large eggs
- 200g (7oz) coconut sugar
- 30g (1oz) unsweetened cocoa powder
- 1 tsp smoked paprika

METHOD

1 Preheat the oven to 180°C (350°F).

2 Lightly grease a silicone Bundt pan with olive oil. Alternatively, use a 23-cm (9-inch) round cake pan; however, a Bundt pan works best. If using a silicone pan, place on a sturdy metal baking sheet. If using a round cake pan, line a greased pan with a 23-cm (9-inch) circle of baking parchment.

3 In a small saucepan over medium-low heat, combine butter and cream. When butter is melted, add bittersweet chocolate and stir constantly for about 10 to 15 minutes, or until melted. Remove from heat.

4 In a medium bowl, beat eggs, coconut sugar, and unsweetened cocoa powder. Slowly drizzle in chocolate mixture, and whisk until fully combined.

5 Pour batter into the greased pan. Sprinkle with smoked paprika and leave to sit for 5 minutes.

6 Place the pan (on the baking sheet, if silicone) in the oven and bake for 40 to 50 minutes, or until a skewer inserted into cake comes out clean.

7 Remove cake from the oven and leave to cool completely. Invert pan over a serving plate and gently remove the pan from cake. Slice before serving.

EACH SERVING HAS:

Calories	Total Fat	Carbohydrate	Protein
255	20g	21g	3g

Chewy apricots and scented orange blossom water flavour these delicious no-bake **Paleo** "cookies."

Apricot Macadamia
Balls

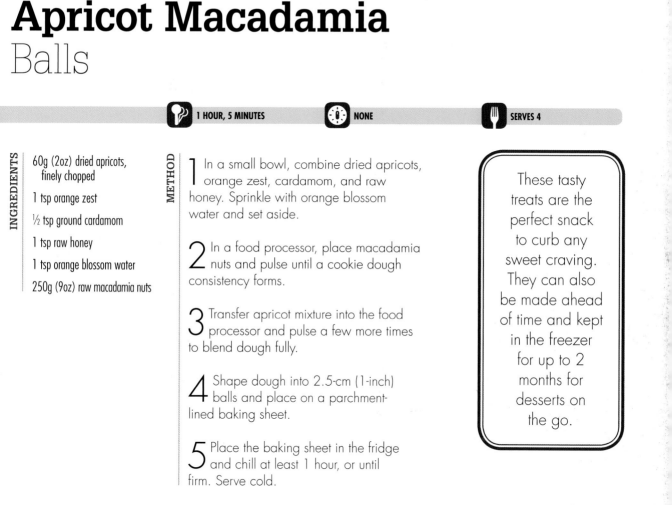

1 HOUR, 5 MINUTES   **NONE**   **SERVES 4**

INGREDIENTS

60g (2oz) dried apricots, finely chopped

1 tsp orange zest

½ tsp ground cardamom

1 tsp raw honey

1 tsp orange blossom water

250g (9oz) raw macadamia nuts

METHOD

1 In a small bowl, combine dried apricots, orange zest, cardamom, and raw honey. Sprinkle with orange blossom water and set aside.

2 In a food processor, place macadamia nuts and pulse until a cookie dough consistency forms.

3 Transfer apricot mixture into the food processor and pulse a few more times to blend dough fully.

4 Shape dough into 2.5-cm (1-inch) balls and place on a parchment-lined baking sheet.

5 Place the baking sheet in the fridge and chill at least 1 hour, or until firm. Serve cold.

These tasty treats are the perfect snack to curb any sweet craving. They can also be made ahead of time and kept in the freezer for up to 2 months for desserts on the go.

EACH SERVING HAS:

Calories **149**   Total Fat **11g**   Carbohydrate **13g**   Protein **2g**

Index

Photo Credits

Page 10
Steve Gorton © Dorling Kindersley
Dave King © Dorling Kindersley
Simon Smith © Dorling Kindersley
Philip Dowell © Dorling Kindersley
Gerard Brown © Dorling Kindersley

Page 11
Steve Gorton © Dorling Kindersley
Roger Dixon © Dorling Kindersley
Will Heap © Dorling Kindersley
Stephen Oliver © Dorling Kindersley

Page 14
Philip Dowell © Dorling Kindersley
Dave King © Dorling Kindersley
Will Heap © Dorling Kindersley
Steve Gorton © Dorling Kindersley
Roger Dixon © Dorling Kindersley
Gerard Brown © Dorling Kindersley

Page 15
Dave King © Dorling Kindersley
Geoff Dann © Dorling Kindersley
William Reavell © Dorling Kindersley

Page 16-17
Emma Firth © Dorling Kindersley

Page 22
Roger Dixon © Dorling Kindersley
Ian O'Leary © Dorling Kindersley
Philip Dowell © Dorling Kindersley
John Whittaker © Dorling Kindersley

Page 23
Charlotte Tolhurst © Dorling Kindersley
David Murray © Dorling Kindersley
Roger Dixon © Dorling Kindersley

Author's Acknowledgments

First and foremost, thanks to my husband, Jason, for the countless hours of recipe writing, testing, food styling, photography, editing, and nutritional analysis. This book would not exist without your encouragement, expertise, and artistic eye.

Thanks to my family in Wisconsin – Mom and Dad, Matt, Sara, Emelia, Ambrose, Estella, and Eleanor. Thanks for teaching me to truly appreciate the food I am nourished with.

Special thanks to Aubrie Weber for helping with recipe formatting, and to Amy Fitzgerald for "falling on the sword" with aubergine recipe testing.

Thanks to Brook, Kayla, Becky, and everyone at Penguin Random House who worked to see this book through to completion.

Special Thanks to the Technical Reviewer

Mediterranean Paleo Cookbook was reviewed by an expert who double-checked the accuracy of what's presented here to help us ensure learning about the Mediterranean Paleo diet is as easy as it gets. Special thanks are extended to Carolyn Doyle.

TEAM FOR ALPHA BOOKS
Publisher: Mike Sanders
Associate Publisher: Billy Fields
Senior Acquisitions Editor: Brook Farling
Cover and Book Designer: Becky Batchelor
Development Editor: Kayla Dugger
Production Editor: Jana M. Stefanciosa
Compositor: Ayanna Lacey
Proofreader: Krista Hansing Editorial Services
Indexer: Johnna VanHoose Dinse

DK UK
Editor: Claire Cross
Anglicizer: Victoria Heyworth-Dunne
Editorial Assistant: Amy Slack
Senior Art Editor: Anne Fisher
Design Assistant: Rehan Abdul
Jacket Designer: Amy Keast
Senior Producer, Pre-Production: Tony Phipps
Producer: Stephanie McConnell
Creative Technical Support: Sonia Charbonnier
Managing Editor: Stephanie Farrow
Managing Art Editor: Christine Keilty

First published by Penguin Group (USA) Inc. in 2015

First published in Great Britain in 2016 by
Dorling Kindersley Limited,
80 Strand, London WC2R 0RL

A CIP catalogue record for this book
is available from the British Library.
ISBN: 978-0-2412-4071-7

Printed and bound in China.

All images © Dorling Kindersley Limited
For further information see: www.dkimages.com

A WORLD OF IDEAS:
SEE ALL THERE IS TO KNOW

www.dk.com